GLENCOE MATHEMATICS

Teaching Algebra with Manipulatives

For use with
Glencoe Algebra 1
Glencoe Algebra 2

Glencoe McGraw-Hill

New York, New York
Columbus, Ohio
Chicago, Illinois
Peoria, Illinois
Woodland Hills, California

Manipulatives

Glencoe offers three types of kits to enhance the use of manipulatives in your Pre-Algebra classroom.

- The **Glencoe Mathematics Overhead Manipulative Resources** contains translucent manipulatives designed for use with an overhead projector.

- The **Glencoe Mathematics Classroom Manipulative Kit** contains classroom sets of frequently used manipulatives in algebra, geometry, measurement, probability, and statistics.

- The **Glencoe Mathematics Student Manipulative Kit** contains an individual set of manipulatives often used in Student Edition activities.

The manipulatives contained in each of these kits are listed on page viii of this booklet.

Each of these kits can be ordered from Glencoe by calling (800) 334-7344.

Glencoe Mathematics Overhead Manipulative Resources	0-07-830593-4
Glencoe Mathematics Classroom Manipulative Kit	0-02-833116-8
Glencoe Mathematics Student Manipulative Kit	0-02-833654-2

Glencoe/McGraw-Hill

A Division of The McGraw·Hill Companies

Send all inquiries to:
Glencoe/McGraw-Hill
8787 Orion Place
Columbus, OH 43240

ISBN: 0-07-827755-8   *Teaching Algebra with Manipulatives*

3 4 5 6 7 8 9 10 079 11 10 09 08 07 06 05 04

Contents

iv

Teacher's Guide to Using
Teaching Algebra with Manipulatives

The book contains three sections of masters— Easy-to-Make Manipulatives, Algebra 1 Activities, and Algebra 2 Activities. Tabs help you locate the chapter resources in each section. A complete list of manipulatives available in each of the three types of Glencoe Mathematics Manipulative Kits appears on the next page.

Easy-to-Make Manipulatives
The first section of this book contains masters for making your own manipulatives. To make more durable manipulatives, consider using card stock. To make algebra tiles similar to those shown in the Student Edition, have students use markers to color the tiles appropriately or use colored card stock.

You can also make transparencies of frequently used items such as grid paper and number lines.

Activity Masters
Each chapter begins with **Teaching Notes and Overview** that summarizes the activities for the chapter and includes sample answers. There are four types of masters.

Mini-Projects are short projects that enable students to work cooperatively in small groups to investigate mathematical concepts.

Using Overhead Manipulatives provides instructions for the teacher to demonstrate an alternate approach to the concepts of the lesson by using manipulatives on the overhead projector.

Student Recording Sheets accompany the Algebra Activities found in the Student Edition. Students can easily record the results of the activity on prepared grids, charts, and figures.

Algebra Activities provide additional activities to enrich the students' experiences. These masters often include a transparency master to accompany the activity.

Glencoe Mathematics Manipulatives

Glencoe Mathematics Overhead Manipulative Resources ISBN: 0-07-830593-4		
Transparencies		**Overhead Manipulatives**
integer mat	centimeter grid	algebra tiles
equation mat	number lines	spinners
product mat	lined paper	two-dimensional cups
inequality mat	regular polygons	red and yellow counters
dot paper	polynomial models	decimal models (base-ten blocks)
isometric dot paper	integer models	compass
coordinate grids	equation models	protractor
		geoboard/geobands
		geometric shapes
		transparency pens in 4 colors

Glencoe Mathematics Classroom Manipulative Kit ISBN: 0-02-833116-8		
Algebra	**Measurement, Probability, and Statistics**	**Geometry**
algebra tiles	base-ten models	compasses
counters	marbles	geoboards
cups	measuring cups	geobands
centimeter cubes	number cubes	geomirrors
equation mat/product mat	protractors	isometric dot grid stamp
coordinate grid stamp and	rulers	pattern blocks
ink pad	scissors	tangrams
	spinners	
	stopwatches	
	tape measures	

Glencoe Mathematics Student Manipulative Kit ISBN: 0-02-833654-2	
algebra tiles	protractor
red and yellow counters	scissors
cups	geoboard
equation /product mat	geobands
compass/ruler	tape measure

Grid Paper

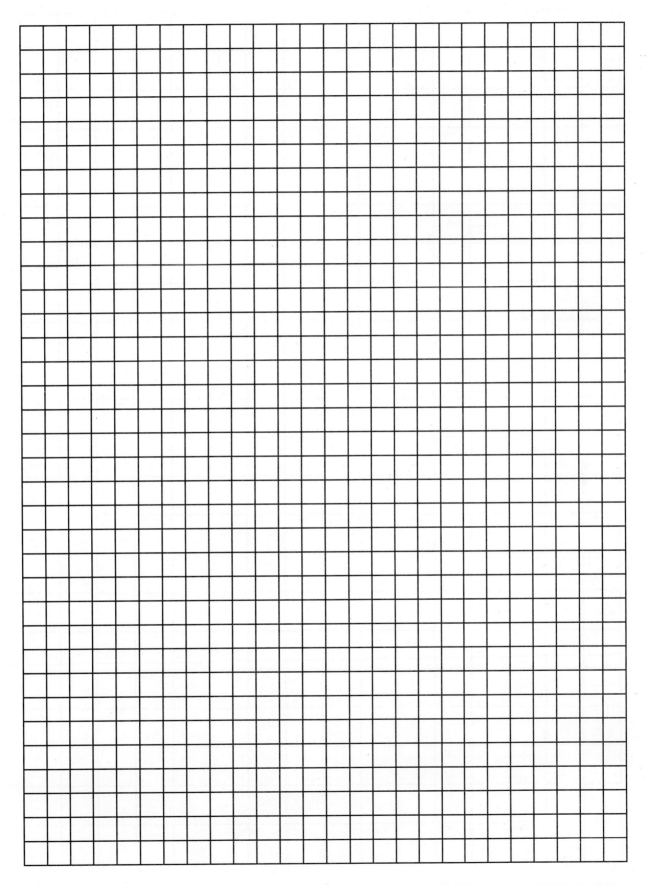

Centimeter Grid Paper

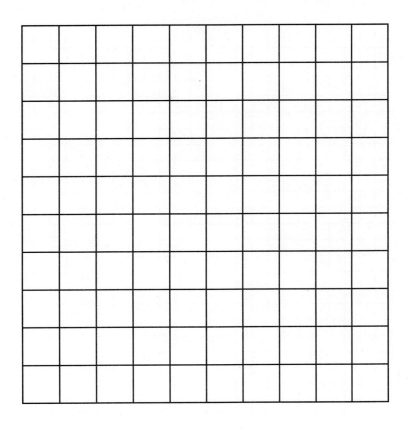

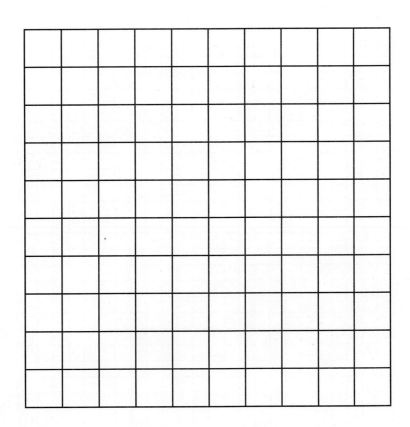

Coordinate Planes

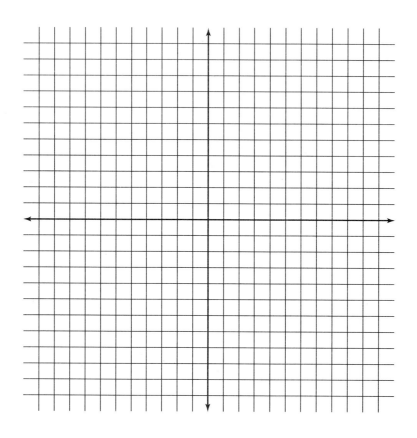

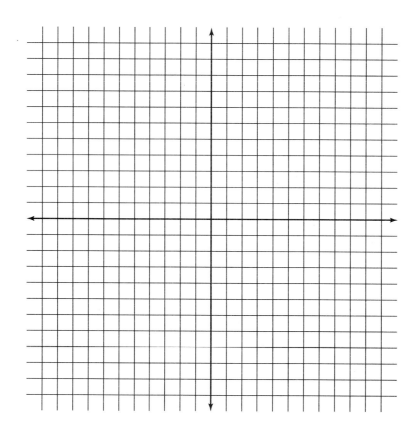

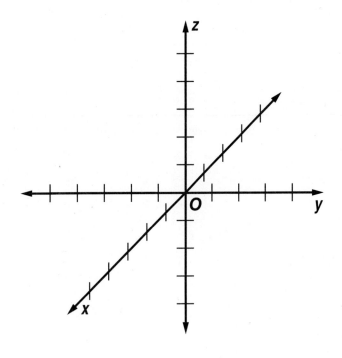

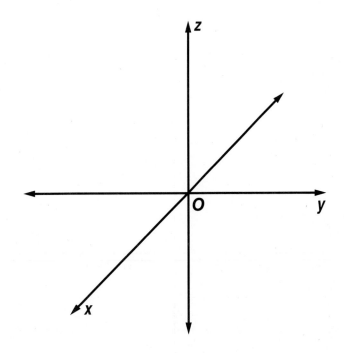

Coordinate Planes for Trigonometric Functions

(degrees)

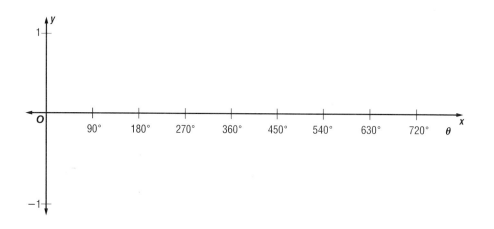

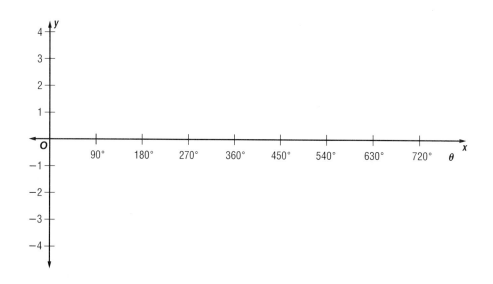

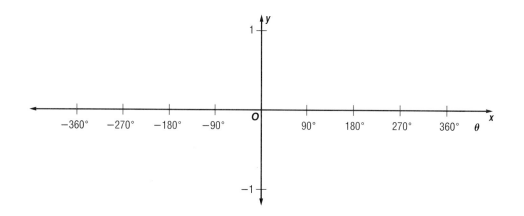

Teaching Algebra with Manipulatives

Coordinate Planes for Trigonometric Functions

(radians)

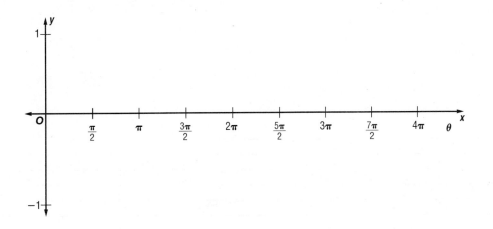

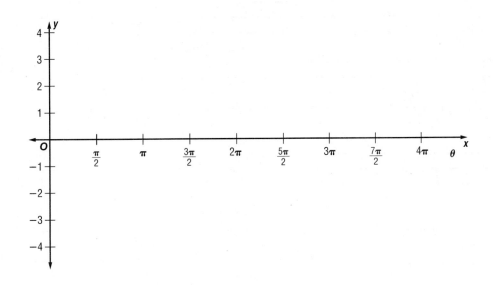

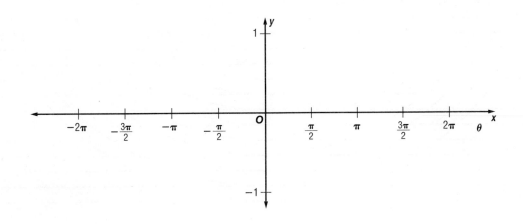

7

Teaching Algebra with Manipulatives

Conic Graph Paper

(circles and lines)

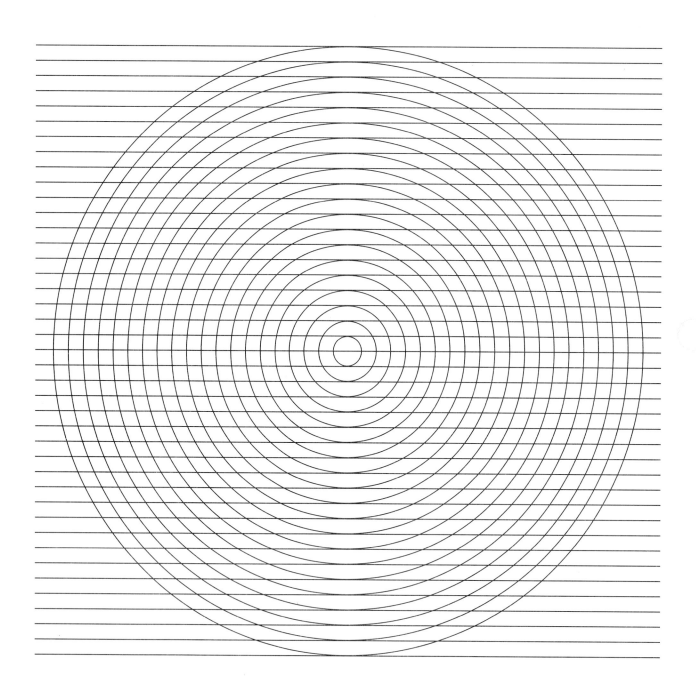

Conic Graph Paper

(overlapping circles)

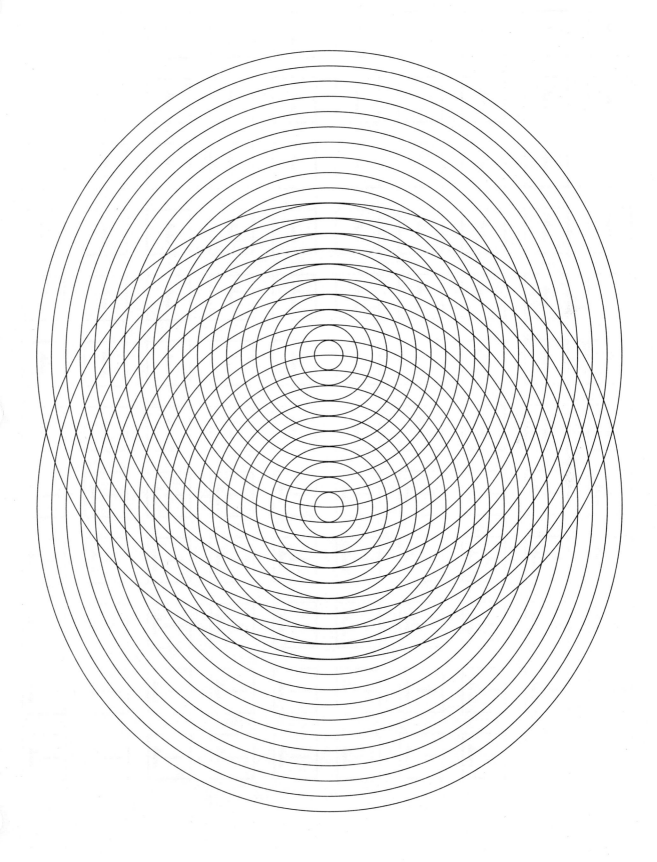

9

Teaching Algebra with Manipulatives

Algebra Tiles

(units)

1	1	1	1	1	1	1	1	1	1
1	1	1	1	1	1	1	1	1	1
1	1	1	1	1	1	1	1	1	1
1	1	1	1	1	1	1	1	1	1
1	1	1	1	1	1	1	1	1	1
1	1	1	1	1	1	1	1	1	1
1	1	1	1	1	1	1	1	1	1
−1	−1	−1	−1	−1	−1	−1	−1	−1	−1
−1	−1	−1	−1	−1	−1	−1	−1	−1	−1
−1	−1	−1	−1	−1	−1	−1	−1	−1	−1
−1	−1	−1	−1	−1	−1	−1	−1	−1	−1
−1	−1	−1	−1	−1	−1	−1	−1	−1	−1

x	x	x	x	x	x	x	x	x	x

x	x	x	x	x	x	x	x	x	x

$-x$	$-x$	$-x$	$-x$	$-x$	$-x$	$-x$	$-x$	$-x$	$-x$

$-x$	$-x$	$-x$	$-x$	$-x$	$-x$	$-x$	$-x$	$-x$	$-x$

x^2	x^2	x^2	x^2	x^2

$-x^2$	$-x^2$	$-x^2$	$-x^2$	$-x^2$

Teaching Algebra with Manipulatives

Integer Models Summary

There are two types of integers tiles.

A **zero pair** is formed by pairing one positive integer tile and one negative integer tile.

You can remove or add zero pairs to a set without changing the value of the set.

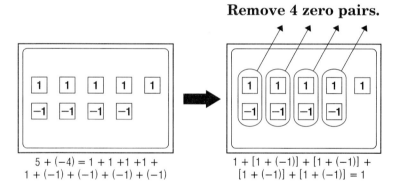

Remove 4 zero pairs.

$5 + (-4) = 1 + 1 + 1 + 1 +$
$1 + (-1) + (-1) + (-1) + (-1)$

$1 + [1 + (-1)] + [1 + (-1)] +$
$[1 + (-1)] + [1 + (-1)] = 1$

Add 2 zero pairs.

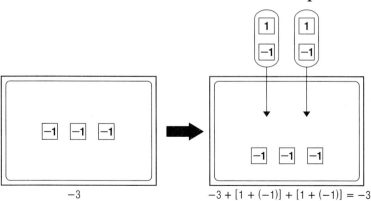

-3

$-3 + [1 + (-1)] + [1 + (-1)] = -3$

Polynomial Models Summary

There are three basic tiles used for modeling a polynomial.

$$1 \bullet 1 = 1$$

Each tile has an opposite.

A **zero pair** results when a tile and its opposite are paired.

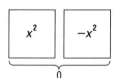

You can add or remove zero pairs to any polynomial without changing its value.

Like terms are represented by tiles that are the same shape and size.

Equation Models Summary

A **zero pair** is formed by pairing one positive tile and one negative tile of the same type.

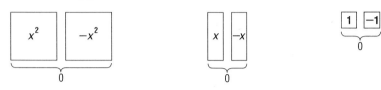

You can remove or add the same number of like tiles to each side of the equation mat without changing its value.

Add 2 negative ones to each side.

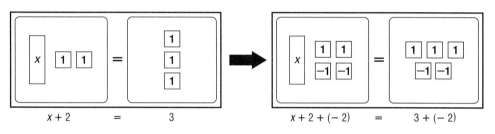

You can remove or add zero pairs to either side of the equation mat without changing the equation.

Remove 2 zero pairs.

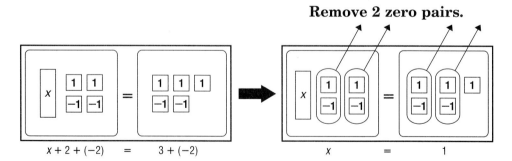

Equation Mat

Rectangular Dot Paper

Isometric Dot Paper

Problem Solving Guide

Problem:

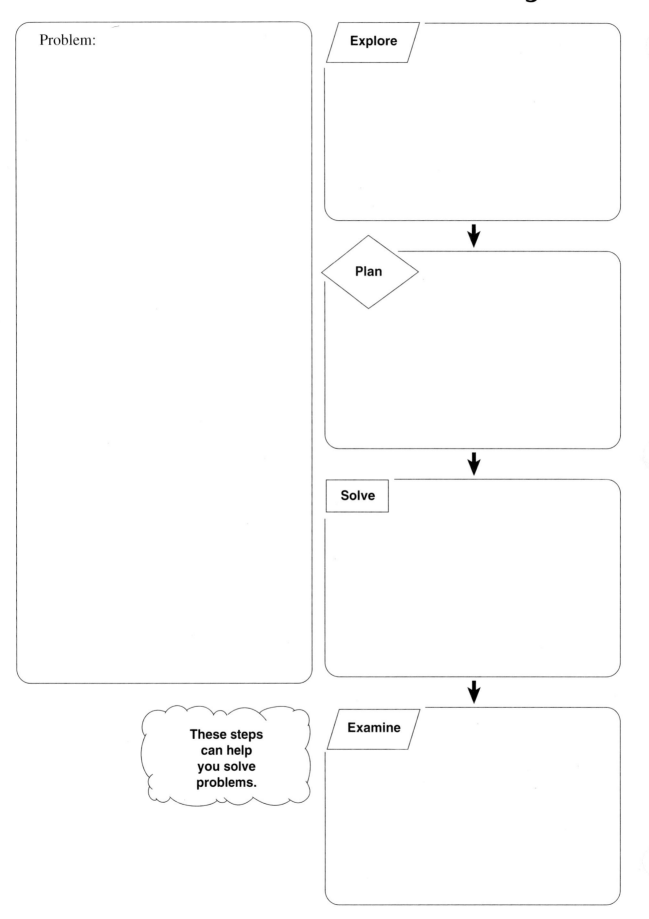

Explore

Plan

Solve

Examine

These steps can help you solve problems.

Teaching Algebra with Manipulatives

Spinners

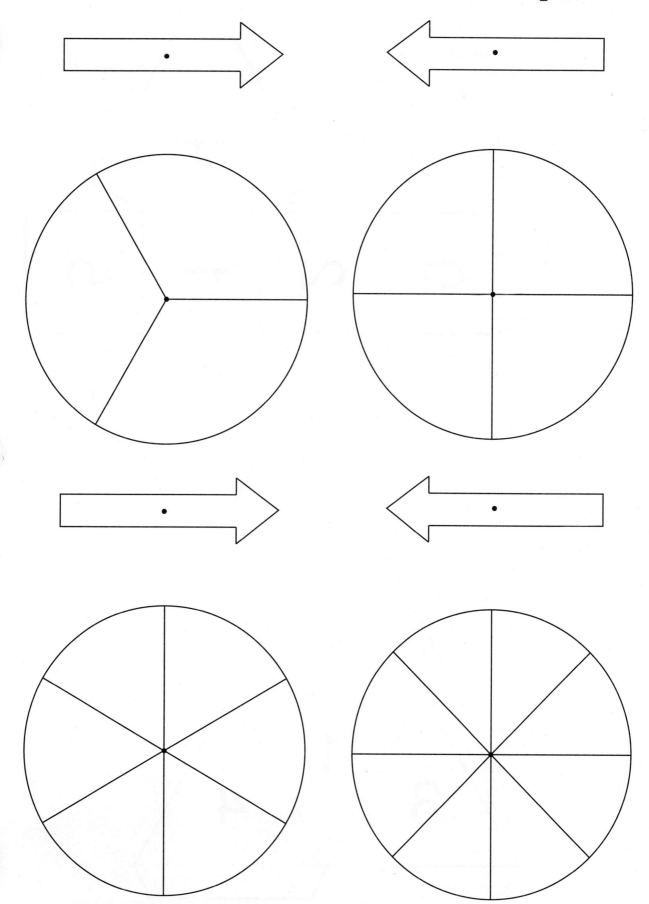

Die Patterns

Cut along the heavy black lines.
Fold on the dashed lines.
Tabs can be taped or glued.

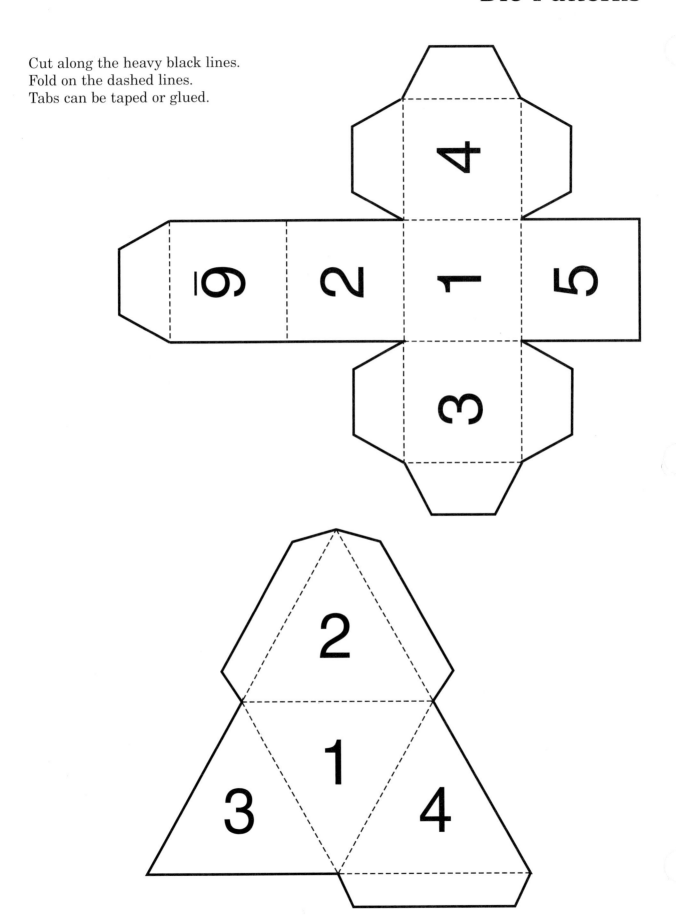

Protractors

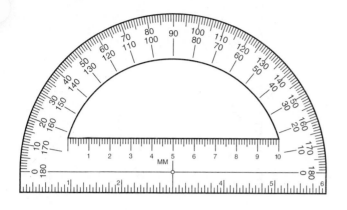

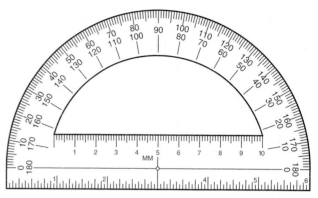

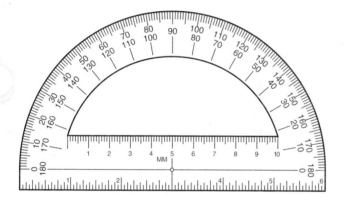

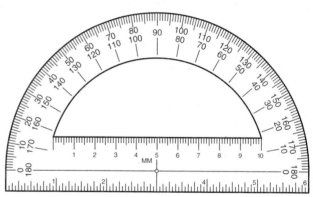

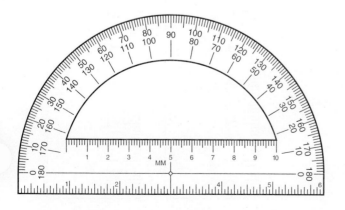

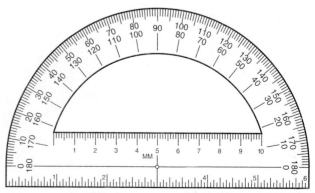

Teaching Algebra with Manipulatives

Rulers

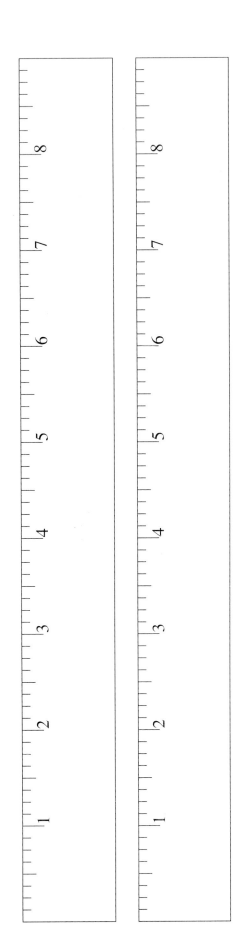

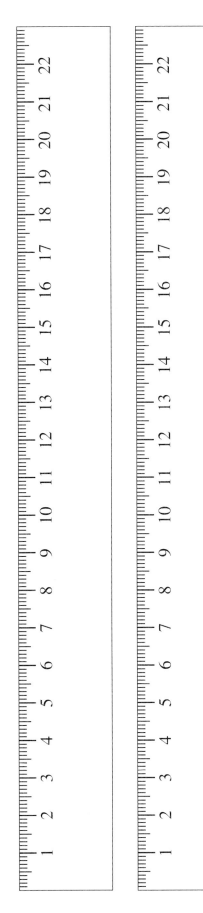

Normal Distribution Curve

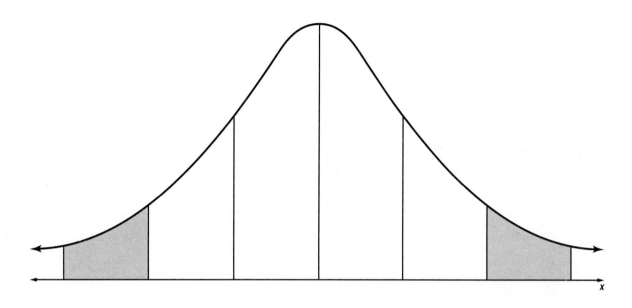

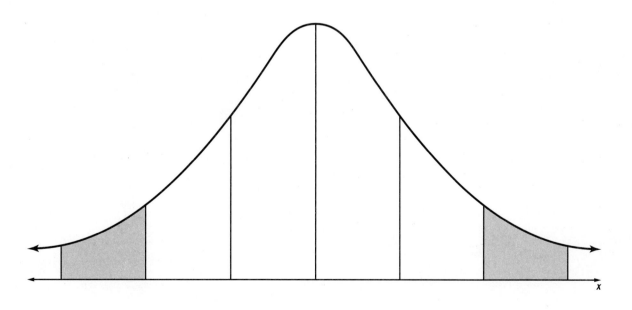

Teaching Algebra with Manipulatives

The Language of Algebra
Teaching Notes and Overview

Mini-Project
Evaluating Expressions
(p. 30 of this booklet)

Use With Lesson 1-2.

Objective To use manipulatives to represent expressions and evaluate them.

Materials
none

This activity requires students to work in groups of two or three to find ways to represent algebraic expressions in a pictorial manner. They then use their representations to evaluate expressions for certain real-number values.

Sample Answers

1. Answer provided on worksheet.

2. Let ◆ represent x.
$3x = 3 \cdot ◆$ or ◆◆◆
$4x = 4 \cdot ◆$ or ◆◆◆◆
$2x = 2 \cdot ◆$ or ◆◆

3. $3x = ◆◆◆ = 4 + 4 + 4$ or 12

4. Let ♠ represent y.
$3x + 2y = ◆◆◆ + ♠♠$
$= 5 + 5 + 5 + 4 + 4$ or 23

5. Let ◆ represent x.
$2x + 5x = ◆◆ + ◆◆◆◆◆$
$= 2(3) + 5(3)$
$= 6 + 15$ or 21

6. Replace each variable by the number given.
Simplify expressions inside grouping symbols.
Find the values of the powers.
Multiply and divide from left to right.
Add and subtract from left to right.

7a. $8x + 3y = 8(5) + 3(3)$
$= 40 + 9$
$= 49$

7b. $5x^2 + 2y = 5(5^2) + 2(3)$
$= 5(25) + 2(3)$
$= 125 + 6$
$= 131$

7c. $3x^2 + 4y^2 = 3(5^2) + 4(3^2)$
$= 3(25) + 4(9)$
$= 75 + 36$
$= 111$

7d. $3(2x + y) = 3(2 \cdot 5 + 3)$
$= 3(10 + 3)$
$= 3(13)$
$= 39$

Using Overhead Manipulatives
Distributive Property
(pp. 31–32 of this booklet)

Use With Lesson 1-5.

Objective Use a geometric model of the Distributive Property to simplify expressions.

Materials
centimeter grid paper transparency*
overhead area/algebra tiles*
transparency pen*
blank transparencies
* = available in Overhead Manipulative Resources

This demonstration contains three activities.

• Demonstration 1 shows the Distributive Property in terms of the area of a rectangle using real numbers. Use this before the Algebra Activity on page 6 (Student Edition page 28).

• Demonstration 2 shows an application of the Distributive Property to validate sums of like terms.

• Extension questions ask students to apply what they have learned to expressions involving subtraction.

Answers
Answers appear on the teacher demonstration instructions on pages 31–32.

Algebra Activity Recording Sheet

The Distributive Property
(p. 33 of this booklet)

Use With the activity on page 28 in Lesson 1-5 of the Student Edition.

Objective Use a geometric model of the Distributive Property to simplify expressions.

Materials
product mat (p. 17)
algebra tiles (pp. 10–11)

Product mats have been provided for the practice exercises. You may wish to have students work in pairs as they complete the activity.

Students may discover that when drawing models for each product they need not trace algebra tiles as long as the units they use to represent 1 and x are consistent.

Answers
See Teacher Wraparound Edition p. 28.

Algebra Activity

Make a Model
(p. 34 of this booklet)

Use with Lesson 1-7 as a follow-up activity.

Objective Use a model to make a conjecture about the volume of rectangular prisms.

Materials
centimeter grid paper (p. 2)
scissors
tape

Students work in pairs to discover the relationship between the volume of a rectangular prism and the corner cut out of the rectangle to form the prism. They make conjectures and look for counterexamples to disprove their conjectures.

Answers

1. $16 \text{ cm} \times 10 \text{ cm} \times 3 \text{ cm}$

2. 480 cm^3

3. $8 \text{ cm} \times 14 \text{ cm} \times 4 \text{ cm} = 448 \text{ cm}^3$

4. $6 \text{ cm} \times 12 \text{ cm} \times 5 \text{ cm} = 360 \text{ cm}^3$

5.

Volume	Square
480	9
448	16
360	25

6. Sample answer: The greater a square you cut from the corner the less the volume. Counter example: a square of 1 cm^3 yields a smaller volume than a square of 4 cm^3.

Algebra Activity Recording Sheet

Investigating Real-World Functions
(p. 35 of this booklet)

Use With Lesson 1-8 as a follow-up activity. This corresponds to the activity on page 49 in the Student Edition.

Objective Graph real-world data as functions to predict future outcomes.

Materials
grid paper (p. 1)

Students will graph data based on the number of students enrolled in elementary and secondary schools in the United States for given years. They then use the graph to make predictions about the number of students in future years. Students will carry out similar procedures using data based on the number of students per computer in U.S. schools for given years.

Answers
See Teacher Wraparound Edition p. 49.

Mini-Project

(Use with Algebra 1, Lesson 1-2)

Evaluating Expressions

Work in small groups to solve the following problems. Problem 1 is done for you.

1. Create a shape to represent the number 1. Show 3(1) and 4(2).
   Let ♥ represent 1.
   3(1) = 3 · ♥ or ♥♥♥
   4(2) = 4 · ♥♥ or ♥♥♥♥♥♥♥♥

2. Create a shape to represent x. Show $3x$, $4x$, and $2x$.

3. Show $3x$ from Exercise 2. Replace each x by 4. Write the value.

4. Create a shape to represent y. Show $3x$ from Exercise 2. Then show $3x + 2y$. Replace each x by 5 and each y by 4. Find the value.

5. Create a shape to represent x. Show $2x + 5x$. Replace x by 3. Find the value.

6. List the steps you would use to evaluate, or find the value of, an expression.

7. Use the steps you listed in Exercise 6 to see whether you get the correct value for each expression. (Replace each x by 5 and each y by 3.)

Expression	a. $8x + 3y$	b. $5x^2 + 2y$	c. $3x^2 + 4y^2$	d. $3(2x + y)$
Value	49	131	111	39

   a.

   b.

   c.

   d.

Using Overhead Manipulatives

(Use with Algebra 1, Lesson 1-5)

The Distributive Property

> **Objective** Use a geometric model of the Distributive Property to simplify expressions.
>
> **Materials**
> - centimeter grid paper transparency*
> - overhead area tiles*
> - transparency pen*
> - blank transparencies * = available in Overhead Manipulative Resources

Demonstration 1
Using Area to Demonstrate the Distributive Property

- Remind students that the area of a rectangle is the product of its length and width. On the centimeter grid paper, draw a 9 × 14 rectangle and label the length and width. Ask students how to find the area of the rectangle. **9 × 14 = 126**

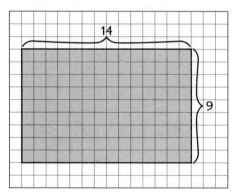

- Draw a dashed line separating the length into sections of 10 and 4 units. Label each section. Ask students how they can use the two rectangles to find the area of the 9 × 14 rectangle. **Find 9 × 4 and 9 × 10 and add them: 36 + 90 = 126.**

- Below the rectangle, write the equation 9 · (10 + 4) = (9 · 10) + (9 · 4).
Ask students what the models shows. **Sample answer: When you multiply a number times a sum the result is the sum of the products of the number and each part being added.**

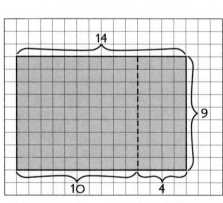

9 × (10 + 4) = (9 × 10) + (9 × 4)

- Use a blank transparency to trace the 9 × 14 rectangle and dashed line. Also include the 9, 10, and 4 labels. Then change the 9, 10, and 4 labels to *a, b,* and *c.* Ask students to restate the equation using the variables. **a(b + c) = a · b + a · c or a(b + c) = ab + ac**

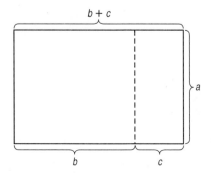

(continued on the next page)

Demonstration 2
Using Algebra and the Distributive Property to Simplify Expressions

- Show students an x-tile. Tell them that it is 1 unit wide and x units long. Ask them to state the area of the x-tile. **x square units**

- On a blank transparency, place 5 x-tiles to form two rectangles. Label them as shown. Ask students to state the area of each rectangle. **3x and 2x square units**

- Write "$3x + 2x = ?$" below the model. Then push the tiles together to form one large rectangle. Ask students to state the area of the large rectangle. **5x square units** Complete the equation "$3x + 2x = (3 + 2)x$ or $5x$". Tell students that this is an example of using the Distributive Property to simplify expressions with variables.

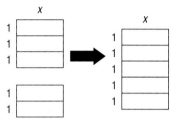

Extension
Modeling to Simplify Expressions by Using Subtraction

Ask students to suggest ways to model and simplify each expression by using subtraction.

- $8(17)$

  Sample answer: Draw an 8 × 17 rectangle. Draw dashed lines to extend the rectangle to 8 × 20. The area of the 8 × 17 rectangle is (8 · 20) − (8 · 3) = 160 − 24 or 136.

- $10x - 4x$

  Sample answer: Show 10 x-tiles forming a rectangle. Separate 4 of them from the others. The models shows 10x less (or minus) 4x. That is, 10x − 4x = (10 − 4)x or 6x.

NAME _____ DATE _____ PERIOD ____

Algebra Activity Recording Sheet

(Use with the activity on page 28 in Lesson 1-5 of the Student Edition.)

The Distributive Property

Materials: product mat, algebra tiles

Model and Analyze
Find each product by using algebra tiles.

1. $2(x + 1)$

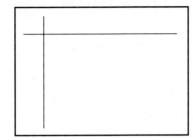

2. $5(x + 2)$

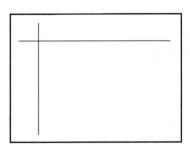

3. $2(2x + 1)$

Tell whether each statement is true or false. Justify your answer with algebra tiles and a drawing.

4. $3(x + 3) = 3x + 3$

5. $x(3 + 2) = 3x + 2x$

Make a Conjecture
6. Rachel says that $3(x + 4) = 3x + 12$, but Jose says that $3(x + 4) = 3x + 4$.
Use words and models to explain who is correct and why.

Algebra Activity

(Use with Algebra 1, Lesson 1-7)

Make A Model

Materials: centimeter grid paper, scissors, tape

Problem: Scott has a sheet of centimeter grid paper that measures
16 centimeters by 22 centimeters. He cuts a square out of each
corner that measures 9 square centimeters. He folds the paper to
form a tray. What is the volume of the tray?

Mathematical data: Volume (V) of a rectangular prism = length (ℓ) ×
width (w) × height (h).

Make a model of the box using grid paper. Cut out a 16-by-22 centimeter
rectangle. Before cutting out the squares in each corner, think about the
dimensions of the square. $9 = 3 \times 3$, so cut a 3-by-3 centimeter square
from each corner. Fold the paper to make a tray and tape the corners.

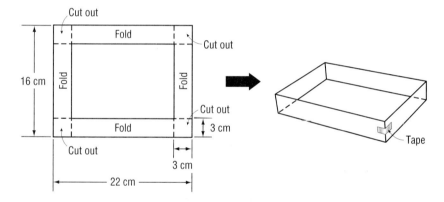

Collect the Data
1. Calculate the dimensions of the tray.

2. Find the volume.

Analyze the Data
3. Use the same method to find the volume of a tray that is cut from a
sheet of 16-by-22 centimeter grid paper. The area of each corner to be
cut out is 16 square centimeters.

4. Suppose the corner cut out has an area of 25 square centimeters. What
is the volume of this tray?

5. Compare the volumes of the three trays. Make a table listing the
volume and the size of the square cut out of each corner to make the
tray. What patterns do you observe?

Make a Conjecture
6. Make a conjecture about how the size of the square cut out affects the
volume of the tray. Add values to your table to support your conjecture.
Try to find a counterexample to your conjecture.

Algebra Activity Recording Sheet

(Use with the Lesson 1-8 Follow-Up Activity on page 49 in the Student Edition.)

Investigating Real-World Functions

Materials: grid paper

Analyze

1. Use your graph to estimate the number of students in elementary and secondary school in 1910 and in 1975.

2. Use your graph to estimate the number of students in elementary and secondary school in the year 2020.

Make a Conjecture

3. Describe the methods you used to make your estimates for Exercises 1 and 2.

4. Do you think your prediction for 2020 will be accurate? Explain your reasoning.

5. Graph the set of data, which shows the number of students per computer in U.S. schools. Predict the number of students per computer in 2010. Explain how you made your prediction.

Real Numbers
Teaching Notes and Overview

Mini-Project
Adding and Subtracting Integers
(p. 39 of this booklet)

Use With Lesson 2-2.

Objective Using models to add and subtract integers.

This activity requires students to work in groups of two or three. Students model adding and subtracting integers. Prior to class, prepare 10 copies of the shape on a thick piece of paper or cardboard or a ditto page.

Have students work the example $-3 + 1$. Emphasize the importance of making zero pairs. Monitor their progress. When students complete the activity, have the students share and discuss their answers.

Answers

1. 9
2. -5
3. -7
4. -7
5. 5
6. 4

7. Sample answer: add the integers as whole numbers; the answer is a positive integer.

8. Sample answer: Ignore the negative signs and add the integers as whole numbers; the answer is a negative integer.

9. Sample answer: Ignore the negative signs and subtract the lesser number from the greater; the answer is positive if the greater whole number is positive, and negative if the greater whole number is negative.

10. 6
11. -5
12. 2
13. -1
14. 1
15. 5
16. -7

Using Overhead Manipulatives
Adding and Subtracting Integers
(pp. 40–41 of this booklet)

Use With Lesson 2-2.

Objective Model integer addition and subtraction.

Materials
overhead counters*
integer mat transparency*
transparency pen*
integer models transparency*
blank transparency
* = available in Overhead Manipulative Resources

There are two demonstrations for this activity.

- Demonstration 1 involves adding integers. Once students have seen you model the three possibilities: 2 positives, 2 negatives, and a positive and a negative, ask volunteers to show on the integer mat transparency how to find the sum of each one of these possibilities.

- Demonstration 2 deals with subtracting integers on an integer mat transparency. Use the same procedure as you did in Demonstration 1. It is important that they know that subtracting a number is the same as adding the opposite number. Summarize the addition and subtraction of integers by displaying and discussing the rules.

Answers
Answers appear on the teacher demonstration instructions on pages 40–41.

Using Overhead Manipulatives
Multiplying Integers
(p. 42 of this booklet)

Use With Lesson 2-3.

Objective Model integer multiplication.

Materials
overhead counters*
integer mat transparency*
* = available in Overhead Manipulative Resources

There are two demonstrations for multiplying integers using the integer mat transparency.

- Demonstration 1 involves finding the product when multiplying a positive integer by a positive integer and when multiplying a positive integer by a negative integer. Ask students to show and explain how to multiply these types using the integer mat transparency. To check for understanding, show multiplications on the mat and have students state the multiplication sentence illustrated.

- Demonstration 2 shows multiplying a negative integer by a positive integer. Be sure that students understand that $(-2)(+5)$ means take out two sets of 5 positive counters. Do additional examples on the mat.

Answers
Answers appear on the teacher demonstration instructions on page 42.

Algebra Activity

Multiplying and Dividing Rational Numbers
(pp. 43–44 of this booklet)

Use With Lesson 2-4.

Objective Multiplying and dividing rational numbers.

Materials
video camera, videotape, VCR, television, a transparency on multiplying and dividing rational numbers, a classroom set of Algebra Activity worksheets on multiplying and dividing rational numbers

Before doing this activity, you may want to videotape students moving forward and backward for several minutes each way.

Display the Algebra Activity Transparency on the overhead projector revealing one rule at a time. Play the videotape corresponding to the rule displayed and discuss rational number products. Students should notice that since the length of the tape playing forward or backward had no effect on the resultant motion, neither will the magnitude of the numbers affect the sign of the products.

Discuss with students general rules for multiplying and for dividing rational numbers.

Next, hand out the Algebra Activity worksheet. Have students work in small groups. Once the worksheet is completed, have groups give their answers and have them explain their work.

Answers

1. -4	**2.** -10	**3.** -12

4. $(+)(+) = (+); (+)(-) = (-); (-)(-) = (+)$

5. $(+) - (+) = (+); (+) - (-) = (-); (-) - (-) = (+)$

6. 300	**7.** -4.8	**8.** -12.5
9. 343	**10.** -16	**11.** 1
12. -400	**13.** 484	**14.** 22.5
15. -18	**16.** -5	**17.** 5

18. -2

19. $1\frac{1}{3}$

20. $20: negative

21. $24y$; negative

22. -8

Using Overhead Manipulatives

Measures of Central Tendency
(p. 45 of this booklet)

Use With Lesson 2-5.

Objective Analyze data using mean, median, and mode.

Materials
transparency pens*
blank transparency
* = available in Overhead Manipulative Resources

This demonstration involves having students identify and collect data. Review the definitions of mean, median, and mode. Students decide which of the measures of central tendency best describes the data.

In addition, students discuss whether the data from their classroom describes the entire school. The Extension deals with analyzing the data to determine what an advertiser would do with the information. Interested students may gather data from other sources, analyze it, and present their findings to the class.

Answers
Answers appear on the teacher demonstration instructions on page 45.

Using Overhead Manipulatives
Statistics and Line Plots
(pp. 46–47 of this booklet)

Use With Lesson 2-5.

Objective Display and interpret statistical data on a line plot.

Materials
transparencies prepared as described on demonstration
blank transparency, transparency pen*
* = available in Overhead Manipulative Resources

This demonstration involves preparing transparencies of a frequency table that lists the average number of times each letter of the alphabet occurs in a sample of 100 letters and a cryptogram that needs to be decoded. Have students identify the number of times each letter appears in the cryptogram. Place a blank transparency over the cryptogram and record the data by using a frequency table. The next part of the activity deals with making two line plots. One shows the 9 letters that occur most often in the cryptogram and the other shows the 9 letters that occur most often in the sample of 100 letters. The remainder of the activity involves decoding the cryptogram.

Answers
Answers appear on the teacher demonstration instructions on pages 46–47.

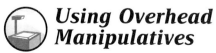

Using Overhead Manipulatives
Experimental Probability
(p. 48 of this booklet)

Use With Lesson 2-6.

Objective Perform an experiment in order to determine the probability of a simple event.

Materials
transparency pens*
two spinners*
* = available in Overhead Manipulative Resources

Have students assist in this demonstration. Let them do the spinning and the recording of the data. After 12 times, have these students compute the ratio of the number of times doubles occurs to 12. Ask students to predict what will happen if the number of spins is increased. Let them do more spins and keep track of the results. Have them compute the same ratio again. Then ask students to summarize the results of the activity.

Answers
Answers appear on the teacher demonstration instructions on page 48.

Algebra Activity Recording Sheet
Investigating Probability and Pascal's Triangle
(p. 49 of this booklet)

Use With Lesson 2-6 as a follow-up activity. This corresponds to the activity on page 102 in the Student Edition.

Objective Compare Pascal's Triangle to listing outcomes and finding the probabilities of given events.

Materials
none

Students will complete tables by listing the number of boys and girls in various size families. Using these tables, students will find the probabilities of families having a certain number of boys or girls. They will then examine how Pascal's Triangle relates to the possibilities for the make-up of families.

Answers
See Teacher Wraparound Edition p. 102.

Mini-Project

(Use with Algebra 1, Lesson 2-2)

Adding and Subtracting Integers

Work in small groups to determine the rules for adding and subtracting integers. Trace and cut 10 copies of the shape at the right out of heavy paper or cardboard. Cut on the dashed lines, too.

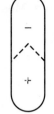

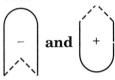 and [+] are opposites. Their sum is zero.

Example: $-3 + 1 =$

Use your models to show each sum.

1. $6 + 3$ **2.** $-7 + 2$ **3.** $-3 + (-4)$

4. $-5 + (-2)$ **5.** $1 + 4$ **6.** $-3 + 7$

7. Write your rule for adding two positive integers.

8. Write your rule for adding two negative integers.

9. Write your rule for adding one negative integer and one positive integer.

Use your models to find each difference.

10. $8 - 2$ **11.** $-6 - (-1)$ **12.** $6 - 4$

13. $5 - 6$ (Hint: Write $5 - 6$ as $5 + (-6)$.)

14. $-2 - (-3)$ **15.** $3 - (-2)$ **16.** $-4 - 3$

Using Overhead Manipulatives

(Use with Algebra 1, Lesson 2-2)

Adding and Subtracting Integers

Objective Model integer addition and subtraction.

Materials
- overhead counters*
- integer mat transparency*
- transparency pen*
- integer models transparency*
- blank transparency

* = available in Overhead Manipulative Resources

Demonstration 1
Adding Integers

- Tell students that in these demonstrations, yellow counters represent positive integers and red counters represent negative integers.

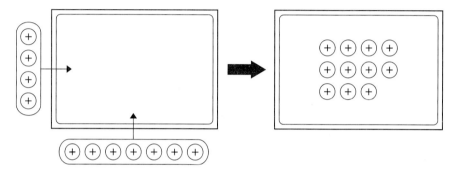

- Place 7 positive counters on the mat. Then place 4 positive counters on the mat. Ask students to state the addition sentence modeled. **7 + 4 = 11** Write the sentence on the blank transparency.

- Clear the mat. Place 7 negative counters on the mat. Then place 4 negative counters on the mat. Ask students to state the integer addition sentence you have modeled. **−7 + (−4) = −11** Write the sentence.

- Ask them to make a general statement about adding integers with the same sign. **Sample answer: find the sum of the absolute values of the addends; the sign of the sum is the same as that of the addends.**

- Clear the mat. Ask students how to show −7 on the mat. **7 red counters** Place 7 negative counters on the mat. Ask students how to show +4 on the mat. **4 yellow counters** Place 4 positive counters on the mat. What sum is modeled? **−7 + 4**

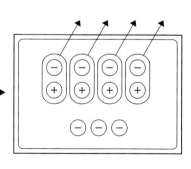

- Tell students, "When you pair a positive counter with a negative counter, the result is called a **zero pair**. You can add or remove zero pairs without changing the value of the set."

- Remove the 4 zero pairs from the mat. Then ask what remains on the mat. **3 negative counters or −3** Write −7 + 4 = −3.

- Repeat for $7 + (-4)$. Write $7 + (-4) = 3$ on the blank transparency. Ask students to make a general statement about the two sentences involving integers with opposite signs. **Sample answer: find the difference of the absolute values of the addends; the sign of the sum is the same as the integer with the greater absolute value.**

Demonstration 2
Subtracting Integers

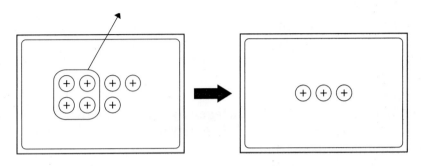

- Show students the integer models transparency. Tell them that these are some guidelines we use when modeling integers. Discuss the properties that allow these guidelines. **additive inverse; additive identity** Replace the transparency with the integer mat transparency.

- Place 7 positive counters on the mat and then remove 4 of them. Ask students what operation is suggested by removing counters. **subtraction** Ask them to state an equation for this model. **$7 - 4 = 3$** Write the equation in the lower right corner of the blank transparency, aligned with $7 + (-4) = 3$.

- Repeat with negative counters for $-7 - (-4) = -3$. Write the equation on the blank transparency, aligned with $-7 + 4 = -3$.

- Clear the mat. Tell students you want to model $7 - (-4)$. Place 7 positive counters on the mat. Tell students that since there are no negative counters on the mat, you cannot remove 4 negatives. Remind them that zero pairs do not affect the value. Place 4 zero pairs on the mat. Ask students what the value of the mat is. Remove 4 negative counters. Ask students to state an equation for this model. **$7 - (-4) = 11$** Write the equation on the blank transparency, aligned with $7 + 4 = 11$.

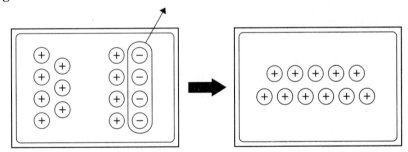

- Repeat for $-7 - 4$. Place 7 negative counters on the mat. Since there are no positive counters to remove, add 4 zero pairs. Remove 4 positive counters. Have students state an equation for the model. **$-7 - 4 = -11$** Write the equation on the blank transparency, aligned with $-7 + (-4) = -11$.

- Ask them to compare the subtraction equations in the right column with the addition equations in the left column. Then ask them to make a general statement comparing subtraction of integers with addition. **Sample answer: subtracting a number gives the same result as adding the opposite number.**

Algebra 1—Chapter 2

Using Overhead Manipulatives

(Use with Algebra 1, Lesson 2-3)

Multiplying Integers

Objective Model integer multiplication.

Materials
- overhead counters*
- integer mat transparency*

* = available in Overhead Manipulative Resources

Demonstration 1
Multiplying a Positive Integer by a Positive Integer, and
Multiplying a Positive Integer by a Negative Integer

- Inform students that you can use counters to model integer multiplication. Remind them that yellow counters represent positive integers and red counters represent negative integers.

- Remind students that 2×5 means two sets of five items. Let students know that when you model integers with counters, $(+2)(+5)$ means to place two sets of five positive counters. Using counters on the mat, model $(+2)(+5)$. Ask students what the product of $(+2)(+5)$ is. **+10**

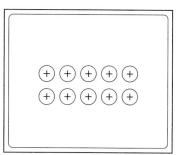

- Clear the mat. Ask students how to model the product $(+2)(-5)$. **Put in two sets of five negative counters.** Model $(+2)(-5)$ on the mat.

- Ask how many counters are on the mat. **10 negative counters** Tell them that this model shows that the product of $(+2)(-5)$ is -10.

Demonstration 2
Multiplying a Negative Integer by a Positive Integer

- Clear the mat. Tell the students that $(-2)(+5)$ means *take out* two sets of five *positive* counters. Place some zero pairs on the mat and point out that you could now remove some positive counters. Ask students how many zero pairs you will need in order to take out two sets of five positive counters. **10 zero pairs** Place a total of 10 zero pairs on the mat.

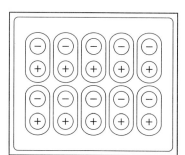

- Take out 2 sets of 5 positive counters from the mat.

- Ask students how many counters remain on the mat. **10 negative counters** Tell them that this model shows the product of $(-2)(+5) = -10$.

Algebra Activity Transparency Master

(Use with Algebra 1, Lesson 2-4)

Multiplying and Dividing Rational Numbers

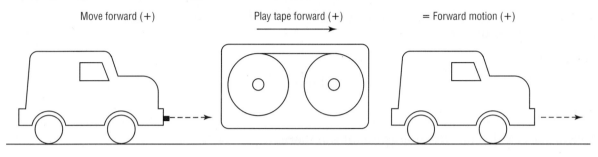

Move forward (+)   Play tape forward (+)   = Forward motion (+)

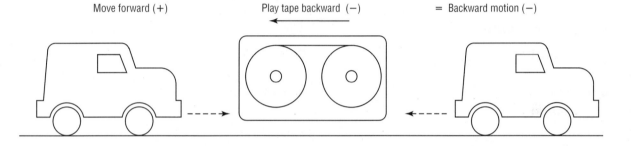

Move forward (+)   Play tape backward (−)   = Backward motion (−)

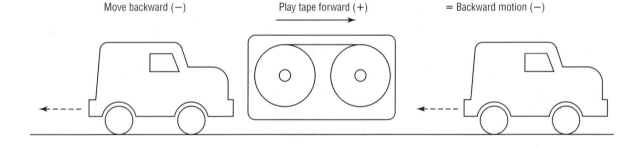

Move backward (−)   Play tape forward (+)   = Backward motion (−)

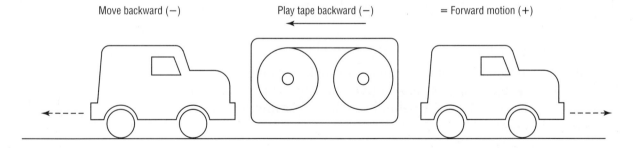

Move backward (−)   Play tape backward (−)   = Forward motion (+)

Multiply.

$(+14)(+20) =$ _____ $(+8)(-12) =$ _____ $(-25)(+6) =$ _____

$(-9)(-40) =$ _____ $\left(-\dfrac{1}{2}\right)(+62) =$ _____ $(+2.4)(-0.5) =$ _____

43   *Teaching Algebra with Manipulatives*

Algebra Activity

(Use with Algebra 1, Lesson 2-4)

Multiplying and Dividing Rational Numbers

In groups, act out, videotape, and play back each product and give the sign of the answer.

1. $4(-1)$ **2.** $5(-2)$ **3.** $(-3)(+4)$

4. State the rules for multiplying rational numbers.

5. State the rules for dividing rational numbers.

Multiply or divide.

6. $(+25)(+12) =$ _____

7. $(-3.2)(+1.5) =$ _____

8. $(-25)(0.5) =$ _____

9. $(+7)(+49) =$ _____

10. $\left(-\dfrac{1}{4}\right)(+64) =$ _____

11. $\left(-\dfrac{3}{8}\right)\left(\dfrac{24}{9}\right) =$ _____

12. $(10)(-40) =$ _____

13. $(44)(11) =$ _____

14. $(90)\left(\dfrac{1}{4}\right) =$ _____

15. $(-3)(-6)(-1) =$ _____

16. $(-25) \div (5) =$ _____

17. $(4.5) \div (0.9) =$ _____

18. $(+6) \div (-3) =$ _____

19. $\left(-\dfrac{1}{2}\right) \div \left(-\dfrac{3}{8}\right) =$ _____

20. Suppose you wrote 4 checks for $5.00. How much money did you   _____
spend?

Is your answer a positive or negative number?   _____

21. Taylor High School's defensive lineman sacked North High   _____
School's quarterback in 3 consecutive plays for lost yardage of
8 yards each play. How far behind the line of scrimmage is
North High School?

Is the lost yardage a positive or negative number?   _____

22. During the 4 day U.S. Open Golf Tournament, Jack   _____
Nicklaus finished 2 under par each day. What number
represented Jack's score at the end of the tournament?

Using Overhead Manipulatives
(Use with Algebra 1, Lesson 2-5)

Measures of Central Tendency

Objective Analyze data using mean, median and mode.

Materials
- transparency pens*
- blank transparency

* = available in Overhead Manipulative Resources

Demonstration
Mean, Median and Mode

- Ask students to imagine that they must describe the average student in the classroom. Have them identify some of the characteristics that might describe a student. **Sample answer: shoe size, height, et al.**

- Survey the students. Ask for the following information: age in months, number of children in the family, height in centimeters. Using a stem-and-leaf plot, record the results on a blank transparency.

- Review the definitions of the three measures of central tendency: the mean, median, and mode. Have students use the stem-and-leaf plot to help them find the mean, median, and mode of the three categories surveyed. Ask students which of the three measures best describes each set of data and why. **Answers will vary.**

- Ask if this information describes all the students in the school. **Answers will vary.**

- Discuss the factors that might prevent this survey from being valid for the entire school. **Answers will vary.**

Extension
Analyzing Data

Ask students to suggest ways an advertiser might use the information collected in this survey.

Using Overhead Manipulatives

(Use with Algebra 1, Lesson 2-5)

Statistics and Line Plots

Objective Display and interpret statistical data on a line plot.

Materials
- transparencies prepared as described below
- blank transparency
- transparency pen*

* = available in Overhead Manipulative Resources

Demonstration
Displaying and Interpreting Data on a Line Plot

- The frequency table below list the average number of times each letter occurs in a sample of 100 letters in the English language. Prepare a transparency of these tables.

- On another transparency, prepare the cryptogram shown at the right.

Cryptogram

Letter	Frequency
A	8.2
B	1.4
C	2.8
D	3.8
E	13.0
F	3.0
G	2.0
H	5.3
I	6.5
J	0.1
K	0.4
L	3.4
M	2.5

Letter	Frequency
N	7.0
O	8.0
P	2.0
Q	0.1
R	6.8
S	6.0
T	10.5
U	2.5
V	0.9
W	1.5
X	0.2
Y	2.0
Z	0.07

KF KW DMF WM UOIB MON JNKADRW'
BACV FBQF BACVW OW QW FBA
IMDJKRADF LDMGCARSA FBQF FBAP
GKCC BACV OW.

- Show students the cryptogram. Tell them that the coded message is a quote from the Greek philosopher Epicurus.

- Place a blank transparency over the coded message and have students help you make a frequency table of the number of times each letter appears in the coded message.

A	9	H	0	O	4	V	3
B	8	I	2	P	1	W	7
C	6	J	2	Q	3	X	0
D	5	K	5	R	3	Y	0
E	0	L	1	S	1	Z	0
F	9	M	5	T	0		
G	2	N	2	U	1		

- Have students make a line plot that shows the 9 letters that occur most often in the coded message.

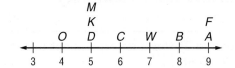

- Show students the letter frequency table. Make a line plot that shows the 9 letters that occur most often in the English language.

- Tell students to compare the two line plots. Ask them which English letter probably corresponds to the letter that occurs most in the code. **E**

- Let them predict the English letter for the most frequent code letters. **Typical answer: A = E, F = T, B = A, W = O, C = R, D = N, K = I, M = S, O = H** Remind them to also look for patterns in words. For example, a single-letter word must be I or a.

- Have students decode the quote. Ask them to suggest possibilities for decoding a particular letter and have them explain their reasons. Record their ideas. **It is not so much our friends' help that helps us as the confident knowledge that they will help us.**

Extension

Many newspapers contain cryptograms. Prepare a transparency of one of them. Make a frequency table of the letters used in the code. Ask students to predict the English letters for the 5 most frequent code letters. Have students suggest possibilities for decoding the message.

Algebra 1—Chapter 2

 # Using Overhead Manipulatives

(Use with Algebra 1, Lesson 2-6)

Experimental Probability

> **Objective** Perform an experiment in order to determine the probability of a simple event.
>
> **Materials**
> - transparency pens*
> - two spinners*
>
> * = available in Overhead Manipulative Resources

Demonstration
Experimental Probability

- Explain to students that rolling two dice can be simulated by spinning two spinners, each divided into 6 equal parts.

 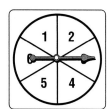

- Spin both spinners twelve times. Tally each time doubles occur.

  Ask students to compute the ratio $\dfrac{\text{number of times doubles occur}}{12}$.

- Ask students what they think will happen if the number of spins is increased. **The probability of doubles will approach $\dfrac{1}{6}$.**

- Complete as many more spins as you wish, keeping track of the number of spins and the number of doubles. Have students compute the ratio $\dfrac{\text{number of times doubles occur}}{\text{number of spins}}$.

- Ask students to analyze the results of this experiment.

Algebra Activity Recording Sheet

(Use with the Lesson 2-6 Follow-Up Activity on page 102 in the Student Edition.)

Investigating Probability and Pascal's Triangle

Materials: none

Analyze the Data

1. Complete the table that shows the possibilities for a three-child family.

3 boys	2 boys, 1 girl	1 boy, 2 girls	3 girls
BBB	BBG	BGG	GGG

2. Make your own table to show the possibilities for a four-child family.

3. List the total number of possibilities for a one-child, two-child, three-child, and four-child family. How many possibilities do you think there are for a five-child family? a six-child family? Describe the pattern of the numbers you listed.

4. Find the probability that a three-child family has 2 boys and 1 girl.

5. Find the probability that a four-child family has 2 boys and 2 girls.

Make a Conjecture

6. Explain how Pascal's triangle relates to the possibilities for the make-up of families. (*Hint*: The first row indicates that there is 1 way to have 0 children.)

7. Use Pascal's triangle to find the probability that a four-child family has 1 boy.

3 Solving Linear Equations
Teaching Notes and Overview

Algebra Activity Recording Sheet

Surface Area
(p. 56 of this booklet)

Use With the activity on page 122 in Lesson 3-1 of the Student Edition.

Objective Find the surface area of a rectangular box.

Materials
rectangular box for each pair of students
scissors for each pair of students

Group students into pairs for this activity. Provide a box for each pair. Ask students to follow along as you model Steps 1 and 2. Identify the faces of the box, before you cut it. Point out what front, back, side, other side, top and bottom represent. Ask them to state the variable for the length and for the width of each face. Make sure they understand the meaning of surface area. You may want to do Exercise 1 as part of your presentation.

Answers
See Teacher Wraparound Edition p. 122.

Algebra Activity

Formulas
(pp. 57–58 of this booklet)

Use With Lesson 3-1.

Objectives Develop, understand, and use formulas. Improve spatial visualization skills.

Materials
classroom set of Algebra Activity worksheets
transparency master of Algebra Activity
grid paper

Cut the transparency on the dashed lines and color triangles A, B, and C if you wish. In groups, have students complete Exercises 1 and 2 on the Algebra Activity worksheet. Next, display the transparency grid and Figures 1 through 12 on the overhead projector. Talk about student strategies for finding areas. Show

these strategies on an easel, whiteboard, or chalkboard for easy reference. Place triangle A over Figure 1 and triangle B over Figure 2. Have students compare the areas. Then put Figures 1–12 over the grid. Review the meaning of altitude and obtuse triangle. Ask students how to find the altitude of each triangle, and how to find the altitude of an obtuse triangle.

Now remove Figures 1–12 and put triangles A, B, and C on the grid. Draw conclusions and develop and write formulas for finding the area of a rectangle, parallelogram, and a triangle. Display these formulas.

In groups, tell students to complete Exercises 3 and 4. Have groups trade Exercise 4 with other groups to compare answers.

Answers

1. Estimates will vary.

2. For base b and height h, area of parallelogram $= bh$, area of triangle $= \frac{1}{2} bh$.

3a. 8 cm^2; 8 cm^2; 4 cm^2;
4 cm^2; 8 cm^2; 8 cm^2;
4 cm^2; 4 cm^2; 4 cm^2;
4 cm^2; 4 cm^2; 4 cm^2

3b. $8x^2$ cm^2; $8x^2$ cm^2;
$4x^2$ cm^2; $4x^2$ cm^2;
$8x^2$ cm^2; $8x^2$ cm^2;
$4x^2$ cm^2; $4x^2$ cm^2;
$4x^2$ cm^2; $4x^2$ cm^2

4. Answers may vary.

Algebra Activity Recording Sheet

Solving Addition and Subtraction Equations
(p. 59 of this booklet)

Use With Lesson 3-2 as a preview activity. This corresponds to the activity on page 127 in the Student Edition.

Objective Model solving equations involving addition and subtraction.

Materials
equation mats*
algebra tiles*
* = available in Overhead Manipulative Resources

This activity involves using an equation mat and algebra tiles to model solving equations. Go over the Rules for Equation Models with the students. There is one example you may use to model the process to solve an addition equation and another example to solve a subtraction equation. Be sure students understand the meaning of isolating the x term. Emphasize the importance of getting the x term alone on one side of the equation. You may want to solve additional equations where students can model the process along with you. As soon as students have completed the worksheet, go over the answers to Exercises 1–4 and discuss the answers to Exercises 5 and 6.

Answers
See Teacher Wraparound Edition p. 127.

Using Overhead Manipulatives
Solving Equations by Using Addition and Subtraction
(pp. 60–64)

Use With Lesson 3-2.

Objectives Model one-step equations and solve them by using addition.

Model one-step equations and solve them by using subtraction.

Materials
overhead counters*
equation models transparency*
equation mat transparency*
two-dimensional cups*
transparency pen*
blank transparency
* = available in Overhead Manipulative Resources

There are two demonstrations for solving equations by using addition and two more for solving equations by using subtraction. Each one of the demonstrations uses an

equation models transparency, equation mat transparency, overhead counters and two-dimensional cups for modeling tools. Make sure that students are comfortable with these tools and understand what they represent.

- Demonstrations 1 and 2 involve solving equations by using addition. The modeling focuses on the addition property of equality, making and removing zero pairs, and isolating the variable with a coefficient of positive 1 on one side of the equation. Checking the solution is part of the demonstrations.

There are two demonstrations for solving equations by using subtraction. The modeling focuses on the Subtraction Property of Equality, making and removing zero pairs, and isolating the variable with a coefficient of positive 1 on one side of the equation.

Answers
Answers appear on the teacher demonstration instructions on pages 60–64.

Mini-Project
Using Logic
(p. 65 of this booklet)

Use With Lesson 3-2.

Objective Use logic by drawing circuit diagrams and constructing truth tables to solve problems.

Ask students to read and study the information provided on the Mini-Project page. As soon as students have finished, go over the information by asking students questions about it. Ask questions about *open* and *closed circuits, conjunction, disjunction* and the entries in the *truth table*. Form groups of two or three students to complete the exercises. Then share and discuss answers.

Answers

1–4. See students' diagram.

5. 0, 0, 0, 0, 0; 0, 0, 1, 1, 0; 0, 1, 0, 1, 0;
0, 1, 1, 1, 0; 1, 0, 0, 0, 0; 1, 0, 1, 1, 1; 1, 1, 0, 1, 1;
1, 1, 1, 1, 1.

Algebra 1—Chapter 3

Using Overhead Manipulatives

Solving Equations by Using Multiplication and Division
(pp. 66–67 of this booklet)

Use With Lesson 3-3.

Objective Use models to solve equations involving multiplication and division.

Materials
overhead counters*
equation models transparency*
equation mat transparency*
two-dimensional cups*
transparency pen*
blank transparency
* = available in Overhead Manipulative Resources

This demonstration contains two activities. Both demonstrations use an equation models transparency, equation mat transparency, overhead counters and two-dimensional cups for modeling tools.

- Demonstration 1 involves solving equations by using division. The modeling focuses on $-x$ meaning the opposite of x, dividing each side of the equation by the same value, and isolating the variable with a coefficient of positive 1 on one side of the equation. Check the solution to the equation.

- Demonstration 2 involves solving equations by using multiplication. The modeling focuses on the Multiplication Property of Equality, and isolating the variable with a coefficient of positive 1 on one side of the equation. Check the solution to the equation.

- In the Extension, students are asked how to represent and solve two equations. Emphasize the importance of writing clearly and concisely in mathematics. Have the groups share and discuss their writings.

Answers
Answers appear on the teacher demonstration instructions on pages 66–67.

Algebra Activity Recording Sheet

Solving Multi-Step Equations
(p. 68 of this booklet)

Use With Lesson 3-4 as a preview activity. This corresponds to the activity on page 141 in the Student Edition.

Objective Model solving equations involving multiple-steps.

Materials
equation mats*
algebra tiles*
* = available in Overhead Manipulative Resources

This activity involves using equation mats and algebra tiles to model solving multi-step equations. Have students model and solve the example $3x + 5 = -7$. Once again stress the importance of isolating the variable with a coefficient of positive 1 on one side of the equation. Have students work in groups of two or three to complete the exercises on the worksheet. Ask them to check their answers. Allow time to review the answers to Exercises 1–8 and discuss the answers to Exercises 9–10.

Answers
See Teacher Wraparound Edition p. 141.

Using Overhead Manipulatives

Solving Equations Using More Than One Operation
(pp. 69–70 of this booklet)

Use With Lesson 3-4.

Objective Model and solve equations involving more than one operation.

Materials
overhead counters*, equation mat transparency*, two-dimensional cups*, transparency pen*, blank transparency
* = available in Overhead Manipulative Resources

This demonstration contains two activities that deal with modeling and solving equations involving more than one operation.

- Demonstration 1 deals with solving $3x - 5 = 7$. The modeling focuses on the order of operations in reverse, making and removing zero pairs, dividing each side of the equation by the same value, and isolating the variable with a coefficient of positive 1 on one side of the equation. Checking the solution is part of the demonstration.

- Demonstration 2 deals with solving $6 = \frac{a}{4} + 2$. The modeling focuses on the order of operations in reverse, making and removing zero pairs, and isolating the variable with a coefficient of positive 1 on one side of the equation. Checking the solution is part of the demonstration.

- The Extension deals with modeling and solving a word problem about consecutive integers.

Answers

Answers appear on the teacher demonstration instructions on pages 69–70.

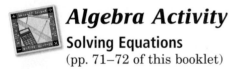

Algebra Activity

Solving Equations
(pp. 71–72 of this booklet)

Use With Lesson 3-4.

Objectives Determine the order of operations of an algebraic sentence.

Solve equations using inverse operations.

Solve equations with more than one operation.

Materials
classroom set of Algebra Activity worksheets, transparency master of Algebra Activity, small object, box for object, wrapping paper, ribbon

Prior to class, prepare an object, box, wrapping paper and ribbon for each group of students. Cut the transparency on the dashed lines.

Have groups of students wrap the object while one student from each group records the steps of the process. Ask the recorder to read the steps backwards or in the inverse order while the other students unwrap the package.

Discuss how the forward and reverse process applies to solving equations, making sure to identify order of operations as a requirement for wrapping the x. Have students complete Exercises 1–3 on the worksheet. Ask students, "What was done to x? What was done to undo x?"

Use the transparency models to demonstrate solving simple equations using a *wrap and unwrap x* strategy. Stress inverse operations to unwrap x from the equation.

Show algebraic solutions to equations without using models. In groups, ask students to complete the worksheet.

Answers

1. add 6; 10

2. add 1 and divide by 4; 6

3. subtract 5, multiply by 2 and add 3; 11

4–10. See students' wrapping process;
4. 15; **5.** −12; **6.** 0; **7.** 10; **8.** 3; **9.** 3; **10.** 6

Using Overhead Manipulatives

Solving Equations with the Variables on Both Sides
(pp. 73–74 of this booklet)

Use With Lesson 3-5.

Objective Model and solve equations with a variable on each side.

Materials
overhead counters*, equation mat transparency*, transparency pen*, two-dimensional cups*, blank transparency

There are two demonstrations for this activity. Each one of the demonstrations uses an equation mat transparency, overhead counters and two-dimensional cups for modeling tools.

- Demonstration 1 deals with solving equations with a variable on each side. The modeling focuses on making and removing zero pairs, dividing each side of the equation by the same value, and isolating the variable with a coefficient of positive 1 on one side of the equation.

- Demonstration 2 is similar to Demonstration 1, in that, it involves modeling and solving special equations with a variable on each side. However, the difference is in the solution.

The first equation, $3x - 12 = 3x + 5$, does not have a solution. There is no value for x that will produce a true statement. The answer is *no solution*.

The second equation is $2(x + 3) - 1 = 2x + 5$. Students find out that any number for x will produce a true statement. An equation that is true for every value of the variable is called an *identity*.

Answers
Answers appear on the teacher demonstration instructions on pages 73–74.

Using Overhead Manipulatives
Proportions
(p. 75 of this booklet)

Use With Lesson 3-6.

Objective Use proportions to estimate a population.

Materials
overhead counters*
lined paper transparency*
two-dimensional cups*
transparency pen*
integer models transparency*
blank transparency
50–100 dried beans or squares of paper
* = available in Overhead Manipulative Resources

This demonstration consists of one activity. It deals with using a model for estimating the population of fish in a lake by way of the capture-recapture technique. Dried beans or squares of paper may be used to represent the fish. A bowl is the lake. Students complete various activities to find an estimate of the fish in the lake. They use a proportion to estimate the population.

Answers
Answers appear on the teacher demonstration instructions on page 75.

Using Overhead Manipulatives
Solving Percent Problems
(p. 76 of this booklet)

Use With Lesson 3-6.

Objective Model and solve percent problems.

Materials
10 × 10 centimeter grid paper*
transparency pen*
* = available in Overhead Manipulative Resources

There are two demonstrations for this activity.

- Demonstration 1 deals with reviewing percent. Then the 10 × 10 centimeter grid transparency is utilized to determine the percent equivalent to one eighth.
- Demonstration 2 involves using the grid transparency to find a percent of a number and to find a number when a percent of it is known.

Answers
Answers appear on the teacher demonstration instructions on page 76.

Using Overhead Manipulatives
Percent of Change
(pp. 77–78 of this booklet)

Use With Lesson 3-7.

Objective Model percent of increase and decrease.

Materials
dot paper transparency*
transparency pen*
* = available in Overhead Manipulative Resources

There is one demonstration that deals with modeling percent of change and an extension that involves modeling and solving percent of change problems. Dot paper is used for the demonstration and the extension. The extension focuses on a common problem that is sometimes misunderstood. Students are asked to decide whether a discount of 20% on a discount of 20% of the original price is the same as a discount of 40% on the original price. The modeling with the dot paper assists the students in making their decision.

Answers
Answers appear on the teacher demonstration instructions on pages 77–78.

Mini-Project
The Music Business
(p. 79 of this booklet)

Use With Lesson 3-7.

Objective Use percent to determine total cost.

Ask students to read and study the information and the example. Let groups of two students work on this activity. Talk about the many expenses involved in producing tapes and CDs and getting them to the consumer. Ask questions about the example to check for student understanding. Some students may be interested in researching this topic more in depth. Have them report their findings to the class.

Answers
1. $11.12
2. $7.19
3. $538.65; $2289.26; $763.09

Algebra Activity
Mixture Problems
(pp. 80–81 of this booklet)

Use With Lesson 3-8.

Objectives Solve mixture problems using diagrams and charts to organize information.

Materials
classroom set of Algebra Activity worksheets
transparency master of Algebra Activity

Cut the transparency on the dashed lines and color Figures 1, 2, and 3 if you wish. Display the transparency on the overhead transparency and examine the mixture problem.

Let Figure 1 represent 9 pounds of $6.40/lb coffee and Figure 2 represent n pounds of $7.28/lb coffee. Place Figures 1 and 2 on the diagram as shown in the chart below.

Then place Figure 3 on the diagram to show that the mixture contains $(9 + n)$ pounds of coffee selling for $6.95/lb.

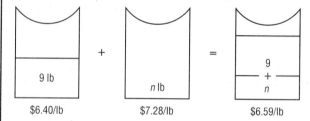

Complete the chart. Discuss how to select necessary information and set up a mixture problem. Practice some similar problems using the transparency.

In groups, have students complete the worksheet.

Answers
1. See students' chart; $(3.10)(15) + (1.95)x = (2.70)(15 + x)$; 8 lb of peanuts.

2. See students' chart; $(0.10)x + (0.05)(4x) = 7.20$; 96 nickels, 54 dimes.

3. See students' chart; $4x + (2)(260 - x) = 700$; 90 @ $4, 170 @ $2.

4. See students' chart; $(2.50)x + (1.50)2x = 396$; 72 adult tickets, 144 student tickets.

Teaching Algebra with Manipulatives

Algebra 1—Chapter 3

Algebra Activity Recording Sheet

(Use with the activity on page 122 in Lesson 3-1 of the Student Edition.)

Surface Area

Materials: rectangular box, scissors

Analyze

1. Write an expression for the area of the front of the box.

2. Write an expression for the area of the back of the box.

3. Write an expression for the area of one side of the box.

4. Write an expression for the area of the other side of the box.

5. Write an expression for the area of the top of the box.

6. Write an expression for the area of the bottom of the box.

7. The surface area of a rectangular box is the sum of all the areas of the faces of the box. If S represents surface area, write a formula for the surface area of a rectangular box.

Make a Conjecture

8. If s represents the length of the side of a cube, write a formula for the surface area of a cube.

Algebra Activity Transparency Master

(Use with Algebra 1, Lesson 3-1)

Formulas

1.

2.

3.

4.

5.

6.

7.

8.

9.

10.

11.

12.

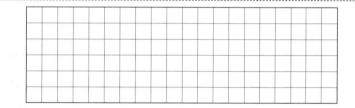

A	B	C

Algebra Activity
(Use with Algebra 1, Lesson 3-1)

Formulas

1. Estimate the area of each figure below. Write your estimate inside the figure.

2. Compare the areas of the triangles with the areas of the parallelograms. Now compare the base and height of each triangle with the base and height of each parallelogram. What conclusions can you make?

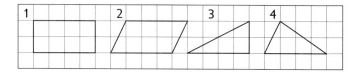

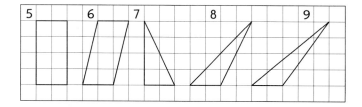

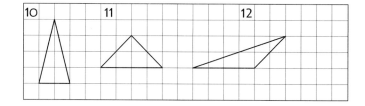

3. Using the formulas you developed for the area of a parallelogram and a triangle, find the area of each figure above when the scale of the grid is

   a. 1 unit = 1 cm;

   b. 1 unit = x cm.

4. On grid paper, draw a triangle, parallelogram, acute triangle, right triangle and an obtuse angle with different measures for their bases and height. Find the area of each figure.

Algebra Activity Recording Sheet

(Use with the Lesson 3-2 Preview Activity on page 127 in the Student Edition.)

Solving Addition and Subtraction Equations

Materials: equation mats, algebra tiles

Model and Analyze

Use algebra tiles to solve each equation.

1. $x + 5 = 7$ **2.** $x + (-2) = 28$

3. $x + 4 = 27$ **4.** $x + (-3) = 4$

5. $x + 3 = -4$ **6.** $x + 7 = 2$

Make a Conjecture

7. If $a = b$, what can you say about $a + c$ and $b + c$?

8. If $a = b$, what can you say about $a - c$ and $b - c$?

Algebra 1—Chapter 3

Using Overhead Manipulatives

(Use with Algebra 1, Lesson 3-2)

Solving Equations by Using Addition

Objective Model one-step equations and solve them by using addition

Materials
- equation models transparency*
- equation mat transparency*
- overhead counters*
- two-dimensional cups*
- transparency pen*
- blank transparency   * = available in Overhead Manipulative Resources

---

Demonstration 1
Solve Equations by Addition

- Display the equation models transparency, along with the equation mat transparency on the overhead projector. Tell students that these guidelines will help solve equations. Make sure that they are comfortable with them. Inform students that you will model each side of the equality in the boxes on the mat.

- Remove the models transparency. Place a cup and 5 positive counters on the left side of the mat transparency. Tell students that the cup represents an unknown value, x. Ask them to name the sum shown. **(x + 5)** Place 9 positive counters on the right side of the mat. Tell them that the mat is a model of the equation $x + 5 = 9$. Write the equation below the mat.

- Remind students that to solve an equation, you must isolate the variable on one side of the equation. Place 5 negative counters on each side of the mat. Point out that this shows an equation equivalent to $x + 5 = 9$ because you have added the same number to each side. Ask what property of equality this illustrates. **Addition Property of Equality** Write $x + 5 + (-5) = 9 + (-5)$ below the mat.

- Ask students if removing zero pairs from either side affects the value of that side. **No, 0 is the additive identify.** Remove the 5 zero pairs from each side. Ask what equation is now shown. **$x = 4$** Write the solution at the base of the mat. (You may wish to have students write each step of the solution as you go along.)

- Model the original equation on the mat. Then place 4 positive counters on the cup. Point out that both sides are equivalent and that this is a **check** of the solution 4.

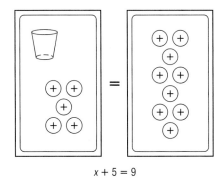

$x + 5 = 9$

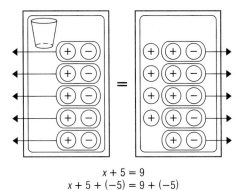

$x + 5 = 9$
$x + 5 + (-5) = 9 + (-5)$
$x = 4$

Demonstration 1
Solve Equations by Addition (Continued)

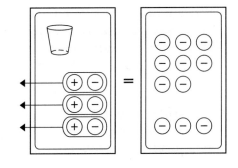

- Clear the mat and blank transparency. Place 1 cup and 3 positive counters on the left side of the mat and 8 negative counters on the right side of the mat. Ask students what equation is represented. **$x + 3 = -8$** Write the equation (and the subsequent steps) below the mat.

- Ask students what you should do to each side to be able to remove all counters from the left side. **Add 3 negative counters, or −3, to each side.** Add the counters, and then remove the zero pairs. Ask students to state the solution. **−11**

- Clear the mat and the blank transparency. Write the equation $x - 2 = 5$ below the mat. Ask students how they might use the counters to show this equation. If necessary, remind them that to subtract an integer, you add its opposite. **1 cup and 2 negative counters on the left, 5 positive counters on the right** Model the equation.

- Ask them what to do to each side to isolate the cup on one side. **Add 2 positive counters to each side** Add the counters, then remove the zero pairs. Ask students to state the solution. **7**

- Ask students how to model and solve the equation $x - 4 = -8$. **Place 1 cup and 4 negative counters on the left side and 8 negative counters on the right side. Add 4 positive counters to each side. Remove the zero pairs. The solution is −4.** Have them draw each step as you model it.

- Ask students to show the check of the solution of $x - 4 = -8$. **−4 − 4 = −8**

(continued on the next page)

Demonstration 2
Solve Equations by Addition

- Write a negative sign on one of the cups. Place that cup along with 4 positive counters on the left side of the mat. Place 9 positive counters on the right side. Write the equation $4 - x = 9$ below the mat.

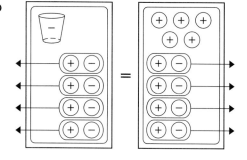

- Ask students what you should do to each side to be able to remove the 4 positive counters from the left side. **Add 4 negative counters to each side.** Add the counters and remove zero pairs. Ask students what equation remains. **$-x = 5$**

- Remind students that to solve the equation, you must isolate the variable with a coefficient of 1. $-x$ has a coefficient of -1, so this solution is not complete. Point out that cups can also form zero pairs. Add a positive cup to each side, then remove the zero pairs from the left side. Write the resulting equation, $0 = x + 5$. Then, add 5 negative counters to each side and remove the zero pairs from the right side. Ask students to state the solution. **-5**

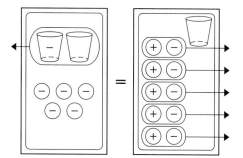

- Show students how to check this solution. Model the original equation on the mat. Place 5 negative counters on the negative cup. Tell students that a negative cup means *the opposite of x.* The opposite of 5 negative counters is 5 positive counters, so replace the cup and 5 negative counters with 5 positive counters. Ask students if both sides have the same value. **yes**

 Teaching Algebra with Manipulatives

Using Overhead Manipulatives
(Use with Algebra 1, Lesson 3-2)

Solving Equations by Using Subtraction

Objective Model one-step equations and solve them by using subtraction.

Materials
- equation models transparency*
- equation mat transparency*
- overhead counters*
- two-dimensional cups*
- transparency pen*
- blank transparency   * = available in Overhead Manipulative Resources

---

Demonstration 1
Solving Equations by Using Subtraction

- Review the guidelines for using equation models by displaying the equation models transparency.

- Place a cup and 6 positive counters on the left side of the equation mat transparency and 5 negative counters on the right side. Ask students to state the equation you have modeled. **$x + 6 = -5$** Remind students that to solve the equation, you must isolate the variable on one side of the equation.

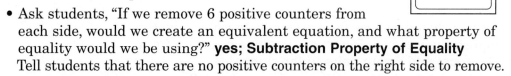

- Ask students, "If we remove 6 positive counters from each side, would we create an equivalent equation, and what property of equality would we be using?" **yes; Subtraction Property of Equality** Tell students that there are no positive counters on the right side to remove.

- Ask them to suggest a way to get 6 positive counters on the right side without affecting the value. **Add 6 zero pairs to the right side.** Add the zero pairs. Then remove 6 positive counters from each side. Ask students to state the solution. **−11**

- Model the original equation on the mat. Then replace the cup with 11 negative counters. Remove zero pairs and ask students if the solution checks. **yes**

- Clear the mat. Write $a - (-3) = 12$ at the base of the mat. Ask students to restate the equation using the additive inverse. **$a + 3 = 12$** Then ask them how to model $a + 3 = 12$. **Place a cup and 3 positive counters on the left side. Place 12 positive counters on the right side.** Model the equation.

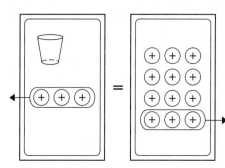

- Tell students that you can remove 3 positive counters from each side to isolate the cup on one side. Remove 3 positive counters from each side and ask students to state the solution. **9** Check by substituting in the original model.

(continued on the next page)

© Glencoe/McGraw-Hill   **63**   *Teaching Algebra with Manipulatives*

Algebra 1—Chapter 3

Demonstration 1
Solving Equations by Using Subtraction (Continued)

- Clear the mat. Place a cup and 5 negative counters on the left side and 13 positive counters on the right side. Ask students to state an equation for the model. **$x - 5 = 13$ or $x + (-5) = 13$** Ask them what they could remove, or subtract, from each side to isolate the cup. **Remove 5 negative counters from each side.** Ask what you would do to be able to remove 5 negative counters from the right side. **Add 5 zero pairs to the right side.** Add the zero pairs, remove the counters, and ask students to state the solution. **18**

- Clear the mat. Write $n - 6 = -11$ at the base of the mat. Ask students how to model the equation and how to solve it. **Place a cup and 6 negative counters on the left and 11 negative counters on the right. Remove 6 negative counters from each side. The solution is −5.**

Demonstration 2
Solving Equations by Using Subtraction

- Write $7 - b = -2$ at the base of the mat. Write a negative sign on one of the cups. Place that cup along with 7 positive counters on the left side of the equation mat transparency. Place 2 negative counters on the right side.

- Ask students what you should remove from each side to isolate the cup, and how to accomplish the removal. **Remove 7 positive counters from each side; first you must add 7 zero pairs to the right side.** Complete those steps and ask students what equation remains. **$-b = -9$**

- Remind students that the variable in a solution must have a coefficient of positive 1. Show students these two ways to complete the solution.

  1) Add a positive cup and 9 positive counters to each side. Remove the zero pairs. The resulting equation is $9 = b$ or $b = 9$.

  2) Recall that $-b$ means the opposite of b. If $-b = -9$, then b must be the opposite of -9 or 9.

Mini-Project

(Use with Algebra 1, Lesson 3-2)

Using Logic

Work in small groups. Study the following and solve the problems.

The circuits of a computer can be described using the laws of logic.

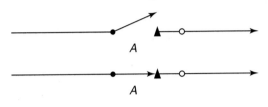

With switch A open, no current flows. The value 0 is assigned to an open switch. With switch A closed, current flows. The value 1 is assigned to a closed switch.

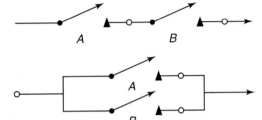

With switches A and B open, no current flows. This circuit represents the **conjunction** "A and B," which we label A $\wedge$ B.

In this circuit, current flows if A or B is closed. This circuit represents the **disjunction** "A or B," which we label A $\vee$ B.

A	B	A $\vee$ B
0	0	0
0	1	1
1	0	1
1	1	1

The truth table at the left describes the truth (1) or falsity (0) of A $\vee$ B for all possible truth values of A and B. In the table, 0 also represents no current flow and 1 represents current flow. Notice that the only time current does not flow through the circuit is when both switches A and B are open. Similarly, the disjunction A $\vee$ B is false only when statements A and B are both false.

Draw a circuit diagram for each expression.

1. (A $\wedge$ B) $\vee$ C

2. {A $\vee$ B) $\wedge$ C

3. (A $\vee$ B) $\wedge$ (C $\vee$ D)

4. (A $\wedge$ B) $\vee$ (C $\wedge$ D)

5. Construct a truth table for the following circuit. There are eight rows in the table.

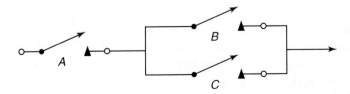

A	B	C	B $\vee$ C	A $\wedge$ (B $\vee$ C)

Teaching Algebra with Manipulatives

Algebra 1—Chapter 3

Using Overhead Manipulatives
(Use with Algebra 1, Lesson 3-3)

Solving Equations by Using Multiplication and Division

Objective Use models to solve equations involving multiplication and division

Materials
- equation models transparency*
- equation mat transparency*
- overhead counters*
- two-dimensional cups*
- transparency pen*
- blank transparency   * = available in Overhead Manipulative Resources

Demonstration 1
Solving Equations by Using Division

- Remind students that a cup represents an unknown value. Ask them how you can represent $3x$. **3 cups** Place 3 cups on the left side of the mat and 15 negative counters on the right side. Ask students to state the equation you have modeled. **$3x = -15$** Write the equation at the base of the mat.

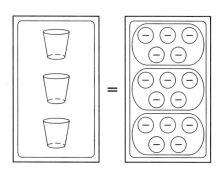

- Say, "To solve this equation, we need to find how many counters are in one cup. To do this, we will match each cup with an equal number of counters." Arrange the counters in three equal groups to correspond to the 3 cups. Ask students what the value of x is in the equation. **-5** Then ask them what "operation" you performed on each side of the mat. **divided each side by 3**

- Clear the mat. Mark two cups with negative signs. Use the cups and 4 negative counters to model the equation $-2x = -4$. Ask students what equation is modeled. Write the equation at the base of the mat.

- Arrange the counters into 2 equal groups to correspond to the 2 cups. Ask students what equation is represented by each group. **$-x = -2$** Point out that $-x$ means the opposite of x. Remind students that the Multiplication Property of Equality states that you can multiply each side of an equation by the same number without changing the result. Replace each negative cup with a positive cup. Ask students to verify that you have just multiplied the left side by -1. Ask them to tell you what to do to the right side to show multiplying by -1. **Replace the negative counters with positive counters.** Ask them to state the solution of the equation. **2** Point out that you solved this equation by dividing each side by the opposite of 2, or -2.

Demonstration 2
Solving Equations by Using Multiplication

- Write the equation $\frac{x}{3} = 6$ at the base of the mat. Show students a cup and ask, "If this cup represents x, what would represent $\frac{x}{3}$?" **Mark the cup with 3 equal sections and shade one section.** Mark and shade the cup, then place it on the left side of the mat. Place 6 positive counters on the right side.

- Remind students that the Multiplication Property of Equality states that you can multiply each side of an equation by the same number without changing the result. To isolate x with a coefficient of 1 on one side of the mat, you can multiply each side by 3. To do this, shade the remaining 2 sections on the cup and make 3 groups of 6 positive counters on the right side of the mat. Ask students to state the solution of the equation. **18**

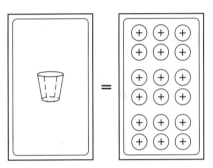

Extension
Modeling and Solving Equations
Ask students how to represent and solve each equation.

- $2y = 15$

  Place 2 cups on the left and 15 positive counters on the right. Separate the 15 counters into 2 equal groups. There will be 1 counter left; to divide it into 2 groups, you must think of it as 2 halves. The solution is $7\frac{1}{2}$.

- $\frac{n}{-2} = 9$

  Place a cup on the left side; divide it into 2 equal parts and label each with a negative sign. Shade one half. Place 9 positive counters on the right side. To isolate n with a coefficient of 1, you must multiply each side by 2 and take the opposite (or multiply by -2). Replace the cup with a whole, positive cup. Make 2 groups of 9 positive counters on the right, then exchange for negative counters. The solution is -18.

Teaching Algebra with Manipulatives

Algebra 1—Chapter 3

Algebra Activity Recording Sheet

(Use with the Lesson 3-4 Preview Activity on page 141 in the Student Edition.)

Solving Multi-Step Equations

Materials: equation mats, algebra tiles

Model
Use algebra tiles to solve each equation.

1. $2x - 3 = -9$

2. $3x + 5 = 14$

3. $3x - 2 = 10$

4. $-8 = 2x + 4$

5. $3 + 4x = 11$

6. $2x + 7 = 1$

7. $9 = 4x - 7$

8. $7 + 3x = -8$

Make a Conjecture
9. What steps would you use to solve $7x - 12 = -61$?

Using Overhead Manipulatives
(Use with Algebra 1, Lesson 3-4)

Solving Equations Using More Than One Operation

Objective Model and solve equations involving more than one operation.

Materials
- equation mat transparency*
- overhead counters*
- two-dimensional cups*
- transparency pen*
- blank transparency   * = available in Overhead Manipulative Resources

Demonstration 1
Solving Equations Using More Than One Operation
- Place a blank transparency under the equation mat transparency so you can write equations below the mat.

- Remind students that, in modeling, a cup represents an unknown amount, yellow counters represent positive numbers and red counters represent negative numbers. Place 3 cups and 5 negative counters on the left side of the mat. Ask students what expression is modeled. **$3x + (-5)$ or $3x - 5$** Place 7 positive counters on the right side of the mat. Ask students what equation is modeled. **$3x - 5 = 7$** Write the equation below the mat.

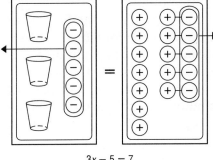

$3x - 5 = 7$

- Review the order of operations. Tell students that to solve an equation, you use the order of operations in reverse. Remind them that you can remove (subtract) the same number and kind of counters from each side of the equation without changing the value of the equation. Point out that, in this case, both sides do not have the same kind of counters. Place 5 zero pairs of counters on the right side of the mat. Ask students whether the value of the equation is changed. **no** Remove 5 negative counters from each side.

- Ask students to state the equation now shown. **$3x = 12$** Write the equation below the mat, below the original equation. Separate the remaining counters into 3 equal groups to correspond to the 3 cups.

- Ask students how many counters correspond to each cup. **4 positive counters** Ask, "What is the value of x in this equation?" **4**

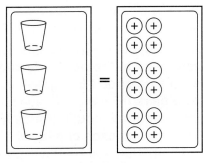

$3x - 5 = 7$
$3x = 12$

- Ask students how you can check this solution. **Substitute 4 positive counters for each cup in the original model. Both sides have the same value, so the solution checks.**

(continued on the next page)

Algebra 1—Chapter 3

Demonstration 2
Solving Equations Using More Than One Operation

- Clear the mat and blank transparency. Write the equation $6 = \frac{a}{4} + 2$ below the mat. Ask students how you can model this equation. **Place 6 positive counters on the left side. Mark a cup with 4 equal sections and shade one section. Place that cup along with 2 positive counters on the right side.** Model the equation.

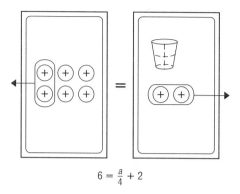

$6 = \frac{a}{4} + 2$

- Ask students what you should undo first to solve this equation, the division or addition. **addition** Remove 2 positive counters from each side and ask students to state the equation now shown. $\mathbf{4 = \frac{a}{4}}$

- Remind students that you can multiply each side of an equation by the same number without changing the value of the equation. Ask them how many groups of one-fourth cups it would take to make a whole cup. **4** Replace one-fourth cup with a whole cup. Then place 12 more positive counters on the right side to make four groups of 4 counters. Ask students to state the solution. **16** To check the solution, model the original equation. Ask students, "If 16 counters are in a whole cup, how many counters are there in one-fourth of a cup?" **4** Replace the partial cup with 4 counters and check that each side has the same value.

Extension
Modeling and Solving a Word Problem

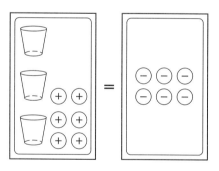

- Present students with the following problem. "There are three consecutive even integers whose sum is -6. What are the integers?" Tell students that you will let a cup represent the first integer. Place a cup on the left side of the mat. Ask how you could represent the second integer and why. **a cup and 2 positive counters; since the integers are consecutive even integers, the second is 2 more than the first** Ask how to represent the third integer. **a cup and 4 positive counters; to represent 2 more than the second integer** Place the cup and counters on the left side of the mat. Then place 6 negative counters on the right side to represent the sum of the integers.

- Ask students to suggest procedures for finding the value of the cup. **Add 6 zero pairs to the right side and then remove 6 positive counters from each side or add 6 negative counters to each side and then remove the zero pairs from the left side. Then separate the counters on the right side into three equal groups to correspond to the three cups on the left. The value of each cup is -4.** Refer back to the original problem. Remind students that you used a cup to represent the first integer, so the first integer is -4. Ask them to state the other two integers. **-2, 0** Confirm by addition that the sum of three even integers -4, -2, and 0 is -6.

Algebra Activity Transparency Master
(Use with Algebra 1, Lesson 3-4)

Solving Equations

  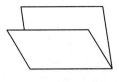  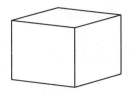

| TOY | BOX | WRAPPING PAPER | RIBBON | PRESENT |

Wrap a gift

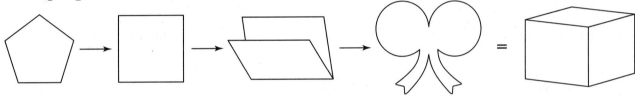

Unwrap a gift

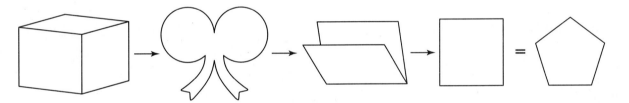

Wrap an x algebraically

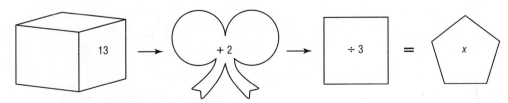

Unwrap x using inverse operations

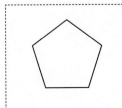  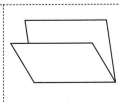  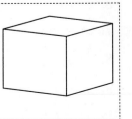

71 *Teaching Algebra with Manipulatives*

Algebra 1—Chapter 3

Algebra Activity

(Use with Algebra 1, Lesson 3-4)

Solving Equations

Example:

What must be done to unwrap x? __**Divide by 2.**__   What is x? ____**4**____

1.

What must be done to unwrap x? _____   What is x? _____

2.

What must be done to unwrap x? _____   What is x? _____

3.

What must be done to unwrap x? _____   What is x? _____

Write a wrapping process for each equation.

Example $x + 4 = 0$

$x = -4$

Example $3x - 4 = 8$

$x = 4$

4. $x - 7 = 8$ _____ $x =$ _____

5. $x + 10 = -2$ _____ $x =$ _____

6. $x + 6 = 6$ _____ $x =$ _____

7. $2x = 20$ _____ $x =$ _____

8. $\frac{1}{3}x = 1$ _____ $x =$ _____

9. $2x - 1 = 5$ _____ $x =$ _____

10. $4x + 8 = 32$ _____ $x =$ _____

     Teaching Algebra with Manipulatives

Using Overhead Manipulatives
(Use with Algebra 1, Lesson 3-5)

Solving Equations with the Variables on Both Sides

Objective Model and solve equations with a variable on each side.

Materials
- overhead counters*
- equation mat transparency*
- transparency pen*
- two-dimensional cups*
- blank transparency   * = available in Overhead Manipulative Resources

---

Demonstration 1
Solving Equations with the Variables on Both Sides

- Place the blank transparency under the mat transparency so you can write equations below the mat.

- Mark several cups with a negative sign. Write the equation $2x + 2 = -x + 8$ below the mat. Ask students how to model each side of the equation. **Place 2 cups and 2 positive counters on the left. Place a "negative" cup and 8 positive counters on the right.** Place the cups and counters on the mat.

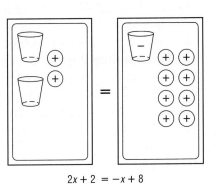

$2x + 2 = -x + 8$

- Remind students that you can solve equations by pairing and removing items from each side. Explain that for this equation you will remove both cups and counters.

- Add a zero pair of cups to the left side of the equation. Pair and remove a negative cup from each side.

- Pair and remove 2 positive counters from each side. Ask students to state the resulting equation. **$3x = 6$**

- Arrange the counters on the right side into 3 equal groups corresponding to the 3 cups. Ask students what the value of x is for this equation. **2**

- Check the solution by replacing the cups in the original equation with 2 positive counters. Remind students that $-x$ *is the opposite of* x, so you will replace $-x$ with the opposite of 2 positive counters, or 2 negative counters.

Teaching Algebra with Manipulatives

Algebra 1—Chapter 3

Demonstration 2
Solving Special Equations with the Variables on Both Sides

- Tell students that not all equations have a simple solution. Model the equation $3x - 12 = 3x + 5$ on the mat. Remove 3 cups from each side. Ask students whether the remaining counters represent a true statement. **no** Inform them that this equation does not have a solution. That is, no value substituted for the cups in the original equation will produce a true statement.

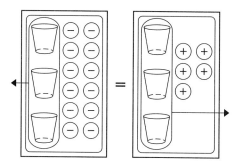

- Clear the mat. Write the equation $2(x + 3) - 1 = 2x + 5$ below the mat. Place a cup and 3 positive counters on the left side. Ask students what the expression $2(x + 3)$ means and how you can model it. **2 times the quantity *x* plus 3; make 2 groups of a cup and 3 counters each.** Add another cup and 3 counters to the left side. Place a negative counter also on the left side to show -1. Ask students if the model shows $2(x + 3) - 1$. **yes** Model $2x + 5$ on the right side.

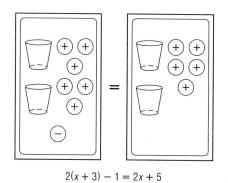

$2(x + 3) - 1 = 2x + 5$

- Remove the zero pair from the left side. Regroup the models so that both sides appear the same. Replace each cup with 2 negative counters to show that -2 is a solution. Then replace each cup with 3 positive counters to show that 3 is a solution. Ask students if any number of counters will result in a true statement. **yes** Tell students that the solution of this equation is all values of x.

Using Overhead Manipulatives

(Use with Algebra 1, Lesson 3-6)

Proportions

Objective Use proportions to estimate a population.

Materials
- overhead counters*
- lined paper transparency*
- 50–100 dried beans or squares of paper
- transparency pen*
- integer models transparency*
- blank transparency   * = available in Overhead Manipulative Resources

---

Demonstration
Model Estimating Using the Capture-Recapture Technique

- On lined paper transparency, prepare a chart like the one shown at the right.

- Tell students they are going to model estimating the population of fish in a lake using the **capture-recapture** technique. Dried beans or squares of paper will represent fish and a bowl will represent the lake. Fill the bowl with dried beans or squares of paper. Ask a student to grab a small handful of beans or squares. Count the number of beans or squares selected and record this number below the chart. Explain that this number represents the captured fish.

Sample	Number Recaptured	Number Tagged in Sample
1		
2		
3		
4		
5		
Total		

Original number captured: _____

- Mark each bean or square with an X on both sides. Return them to the bowl and mix well with the rest. Tell students that this part of the activity is similar to tagging fish in a lake.

- Have another student take a small handful of beans or squares of paper from the bowl. Record the number of beans or squares selected.

- Count the number of beans or squares in the handful that are marked with an X. Tell students this represents the number of tagged fish recaptured. Record this number in the chart.

- Return all the beans or squares to the bowl, mix, and recapture four more times.

- Have students find the total recaptured and the total tagged. Record in the chart. Have students use the proportion below to estimate the number of beans or squares in the bowl.

$$\frac{\text{original number captured}}{\text{number in bowl}} = \frac{\text{total tagged in samples}}{\text{total recaptured}}$$

- Count all the beans or squares in the bowl. Compare to the estimate. **Answers will vary, but the estimate should be close to the actual number.**

75   *Teaching Algebra with Manipulatives*

Algebra 1—Chapter 3

Using Overhead Manipulatives

(Use with Algebra 1, Lesson 3-6)

Solving Percent Problems

> **Objective** Model and solve percent problems.
>
> **Materials**
> - 10 × 10 centimeter grid*
> - transparency pens*
> * = available in Overhead Manipulative Resources

Demonstration 1
Modeling Percent

- Review the meaning of percent. Place a hundred square on the screen of the overhead projector, on top of the blank transparency. Tell students that the square represents 100%. Mark the square into fourths. Then mark each fourth into halves. Ask students what part of the whole each small area is. **one eighth**

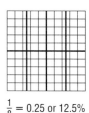

$\frac{1}{8}$ = 0.25 or 12.5%

- Inform students you can use this square to find a percent equivalent to one eighth. Ask students to count the squares in a one-eighth section. **There are 10 whole squares and 5 half squares, or $12\frac{1}{2}$ squares.** Write $\frac{1}{8}$ or 12.5% on the transparency.

Teacher Demonstration 2
Finding Percent

- Place a hundred square on the screen. Tell students that you can use the square to find 40% of 50. Outline 40% of the square.

- Ask, "If the whole square represents the number 50, what does each small square represent?" **1 small square represents the number one half** Shade two squares at a time and have students count as you shade to find the number of double squares within the outline. **20** Write 40% of 50 is 20 on the transparency. Below it, write the equation 0.40(50) = 20.

40% of 50 is 20
0.40 · 50 = 20

- Place another hundred square on the screen. Tell students, "We have used the hundred square to find a percentage of a number. We also can use the square to find the base when we know the rate and the percentage. For example, 20% of what number is 17?" Outline 20% of the square.

- Write the 17 within the 20% outline. Ask students what part of the whole 17 represents. **20% or $\frac{1}{5}$** Ask how they could calculate the value of the whole square when 20% of it is 17. **Multiply 0.20 times some number to get 17; divide 17 by 0.20 to find the number.** Write 20% of ? is 17 on the transparency. Below it, write the equations 0.20x = 17, x = 17 ÷ 0.20, and x = 85.

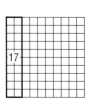

20% of __?__ is 17
0.20x = 17
x = 17 ÷ 0.20
x = 85

Using Overhead Manipulatives

(Use with Algebra 1, Lesson 3-7)

Percent of Change

Objective Model percent of increase and decrease.

Materials
- dot paper transparency*
- transparency pens*   * = available in Overhead Manipulative Resources

Demonstration
Modeling Percent of Change

- Ask students what is meant by the expression *the price of an item was increased by 15% and the price of an item has been decreased by 10%*. Explain that such percents are referred to as percents of increase and decrease, or percents of change. Tell students that percents of change can be modeled with dot paper.

- On the dot paper transparency, draw a 4-by-5 rectangle. Tell students you want to decrease the area by 25%. Separate the rectangle into 20 equal parts as shown in Figure A. Ask students what part of the rectangle each square is. **Since there are 20 squares, each square is one-twentieth of the rectangle, or 5%.** Ask them how many squares represent 25% of the rectangle. **5 squares**

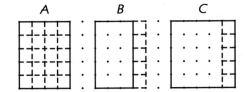

- Remove 5 squares, from the original figure to show a decrease of 25%. See Figure B.

- Refer students to Figure C. Ask them how its area compares to the original figure, and to explain how they determined the percent of change. **increase of 25%; 5 more squares were added to the original figure and each square added was 5% of the original figure**

- Draw Figures X, Y, and Z on the dot paper transparency. Ask what percent of the original each square represents. $\frac{1}{8}$ **or** $12\frac{1}{2}$**%**

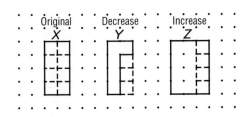

77

Teaching Algebra with Manipulatives

Algebra 1—Chapter 3

• Ask students how to determine by what percent the original figure was increased or decreased. **Y, 3 out of 8 sections were removed so the figure was decreased by $\frac{3}{8}$ or 37.5%; Z, 4 out of 8 sections were added to the original figure, so the figure was increased by $\frac{4}{8}$ or 50%**

Extension
Modeling and Solving Percent of Change Problems

• Present the following problem.

The sale price of an item is 20% off the original price. Today only, the store offers to take an additional 20% off the sale price. Are these two discounts the same as 40% off the original price?

• Draw a 10-by-10 square on the dot paper transparency. Tell students that it represents the original price. See Figure S. Ask them how to show a 20% decrease. **Remove 20 squares** Label the remaining section 80. See Figure A.

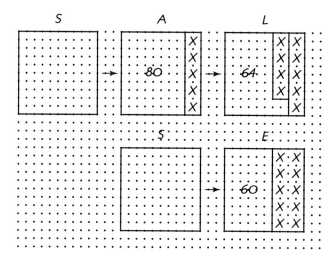

• Ask students how to calculate a 20% decrease in the remaining section. **20% of 80 = 16** Remove 16 squares. Replace the label 80 with 64. See Figure L. "If the original cost was $100, what was the final sale price?" **$64**

• Draw Figure E. Ask students what sale price would result from a 40% decrease in the original price. **$60** Ask whether a discount of 20% on a discount of 20% of the original price is the same as a discount of 40% on the original price. **no**

Mini-Project

(Use with Algebra 1, Lesson 3-7)

The Music Business

Many expenses are involved in producing tapes and CDs and getting them to the consumer. For example, a record company must provide a studio, backup musicians, a producer, technicians, and recording equipment, as well as pay the artist. Then a wholesaler provides storage and transportation. A rackjobber provides tapes and CDs to a number of retailers in an area. And finally the retailer has expenses involved in sales, advertising, marketing, and so on.

Example: A tape costs $4.18 to produce. The record company uses markups to determine the cost to the consumer, as follows.

    a. Record company to wholesaler, 20% markup:
    $4.18 + 0.20($4.18) = $4.18 + $0.84 = $5.02

    b. Wholesaler to rackjobber, 15% markup:
    $5.02 + 0.15($5.02) = $5.02 + $0.75 = $5.77

    c. Rackjobber to retailer, 15% markup:
    $5.77 + 0.15($5.77) = $5.77 + $0.87 = $6.64

    d. Retailer to consumer, 40% markup:
    $6.64 + 0.40($6.64) = $6.64 + $2.66 = $9.30

The consumer must pay $9.30 for the tape.

Answer the following questions.

1. Use the markups given in the example to find the price a consumer pays for a CD that costs the record company $5.00 to produce.

2. If a CD sells at a record store for $15.98, how much did it cost the record company to produce?

3. Each time a song is played on the air, the radio station must pay $0.06 to a royalty society. Of this amount, the society keeps 15% for its expenses. Then 75% of the remainder is paid to a music publishing company and 25% is paid to the songwriter. A network of 75 stations each played "I've Got the Lonesome-For-You Blues" 4 times a day during the first 2 weeks after its release, 11 times a day during the next 2 weeks, 20 times a day for the next 3 weeks, and 8 times a day for the next 3 weeks. How much would the royalty society, the publisher, and the songwriter each receive?

Algebra 1—Chapter 3

Algebra Activity Transparency Master

(Use with Algebra 1, Lesson 3-8)

Mixture Problems

Cathy's Coffee Cafe sells gourmet coffee mixes by the pound. How many pounds of $7.28/lb coffee must Cathy mix with 9 pounds of $6.40/lb coffee to create a mixture worth $6.95 per pound?

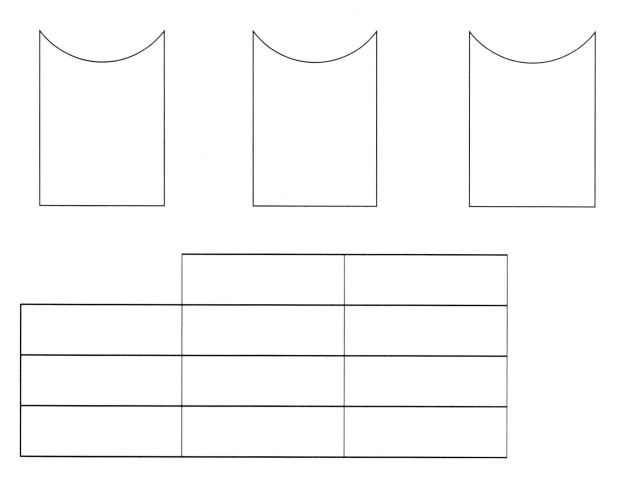

Figure 1	Figure 2	Figure 3

Teaching Algebra with Manipulatives

Algebra Activity

(Use with Algebra 1, Lesson 3-8)

Mixture Problems

Illustrate each problem using the diagrams below. Then complete the chart, write an equation, and solve each problem.

1. Nancy's Nut Shop sells cashews for $3.10 per pound and peanuts for $1.95 per pound. How many pounds of peanuts must be added to 15 pounds of cashews to make a mix that sells for $2.70 per pound?

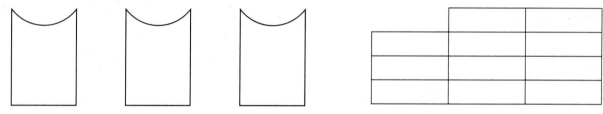

2. Anna has 4 times as many nickels as dimes in her bank. Her bank contains $7.20. How many nickels and dimes are in Anna's bank?

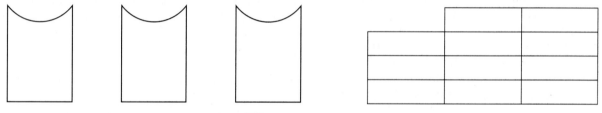

3. Carmen sold play tickets. Each adult ticket cost $4.00 and each student ticket cost $2.00. The total number of tickets sold was 260, and the total income was $700.00. How many of each kind of ticket were sold?

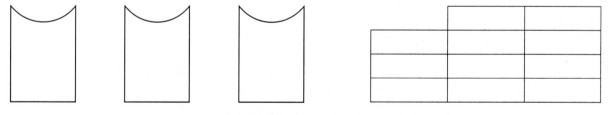

4. David sold carnival tickets for his school fund raiser. Adult tickets cost $2.50 and student tickets cost $1.50. If David collected $396.00 selling twice as many student tickets as adult tickets, how many of each kind of ticket did he sell?

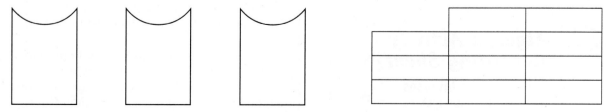

Graphing Relations and Functions
Teaching Notes and Overview

Using Overhead Manipulatives

Relations
(p. 85 of this booklet)

Use With Lesson 4-3.

Objective Model a relation and its inverse

Materials
overhead geoboard*
geobands*
* = available in Overhead Manipulative Resources

This demonstration uses geoboards with geobands to construct triangles. Students are asked to name the points in the interior of the triangles. They are told that this set of points is a relation. Students state the domain and range of the relation. Next, students write the inverse of this relation by switching the coordinates of each ordered pair of the relation. Then students construct the triangle containing these interior points.

In the Extension, students are asked to repeat the same activity for a rectangle with given vertices. Then students compare the size, the shape and the position of the two rectangles. Next, students are given the vertices of a triangle and asked to repeat the activity again. The comparison shows that the triangles have the same shape and size, and are in the same position. Thus, the relation and its inverse are equivalent. Students are asked to experiment with other figures on the geoboard and try to predict the figure corresponding to the inverse of the relation.

Answers
Answers appear on the teacher demonstration instructions on page 85.

Algebra Activity Recording Sheet

Relations and Inverses
(p. 86 of this booklet)

Use With the activity on page 207 in Lesson 4-3 of the Student Edition.

Objective Graphing a relation and its inverse.

Materials
colored pencils

You may want to use student pairs to do this activity or do it as a classroom demonstration with student participation. If you decide to do a classroom demonstration, prior to class, prepare an easel pad with a one-inch by one-inch coordinate grid. In addition, give a sheet of coordinate grid paper to each student. Have a student graph the relation on the easel grid paper with a colored marker. Then another student can graph the inverse of the relation with a different colored marker. In the meantime, students can be doing the activity at their seats. Ask for assistance to fold the grid paper. You may choose to answer Exercises 1–4 with the entire class or have pairs of students work on the exercises.

Answers
See Teacher Wraparound Edition p. 207.

Using Overhead Manipulatives

Graphing Linear Relations
(p. 87 of this booklet)

Use With Lesson 4-5.

Objective Graphing linear equations on a coordinate plane.

Materials
coordinate grid transparency*
transparency pen*
transparency prepared as described on the
  activity
three blank transparencies
* = available in Overhead Manipulative Resources

This demonstration requires you to prepare a transparency like the table in the activity. Do not copy the numbers shown in the parentheses or the heading of the second column. Have students work in groups of two or three. On the transparency, write $x + 1$ in the heading of the second column. Complete the first row with the class. Then have them complete the table and

82

graph the ordered pairs for $y = x + 1$ in their groups. Visit each group to make sure they understand. Remind them to draw a line through the points. Repeat the same procedure for $y = -3x$. In the last equation, $3x + 4y = 6$, you may want to show the step-by-step process for solving the equation for y. Then show the expression for y in terms of x in the table.

Answers
Answers appear on the teacher demonstration instructions on page 87.

Using Overhead Manipulatives
Functions
(p. 88 of this booklet)

Use With Lesson 4-6.

Objective Determine whether a relation is a function.

Materials
overhead geoboard and geobands*
transparency pens*
dot paper transparency*
* = available in Overhead Manipulative Resources

This demonstration focuses on two comparisons. The first one is with the mapping of a polygon to its area, that is, (polygon, area). The second deals with mapping of the area of a polygon to the polygon, that is, (area, polygon). For each of these, is the relation a function?

You may want to conduct this activity with the entire class. Use the overhead geoboard and geobands to illustrate polygon A or you may want to prepare a dot grid transparency. Have students explain how they found an area of 5 square units for A. As you do the activity on the overhead geoboard or dot grid transparency, students will be able to do the activity at their seats. Discuss and display the answers.

Emphasize that a function is a relation in which each element of the domain is paired with exactly one element of the range. Point out that the relation of mapping the area of each polygon to itself is not a function. Have

students explain why. Be sure students understand that all functions are relations, but not all relations are functions.

Answers
Answers appear on the teacher demonstration instructions on page 88.

Mini-Project
Evaluating Expressions
(p. 89 of this booklet)

Use With Lesson 4-6.

Objective Determine whether a relation is a function.

Materials
overhead geoboard and geobands*
transparency pens*
dot paper transparency*
* = available in Overhead Manipulative Resources

This project requires students to work in pairs. One student rolls the die. The other records the data in the chart and on the grid. Once the data is complete, the students discuss and answer Exercises 1–5. You may need to review the vertical line test.

Answers
1–4. Answers will vary.

5. Students may find in individual experiments that the vertical line test indicates that the relation is a function. However, it is likely that sooner or later the relation will prove not to be a function—that is, a result of the red die will be paired with two or more results on the green die.

Algebra Activity Recording Sheet
Looking for Patterns
(p. 90 of this booklet)

Use With the activity on page 241 in Lesson 4-8 of the Student Edition.

Objective Look for a pattern.

Algebra 1—Chapter 4

Materials

scissors
several pieces of string

Prior to the activity cut the pieces of string. Form student pairs. Emphasize the importance of reading the steps to collect the data. Monitor each pair and ask questions. As soon as the pairs have completed the activity, discuss the answers to the exercises. Have the pairs explain their answers.

Answers

See Teacher Wraparound Edition p. 241.

Algebra Activity

Functions
(pp. 91–92 of this booklet)

Use With Lesson 4-8.

Objective Write an equation given some of the solutions.

Materials

classroom set of Algebra Activity worksheets
transparency master of Algebra Activity

Display the transparency master of the Algebra Activity. Discuss the diagram of a function machine. The function rule is computed for each

"x" input that yields "y" as its output. Next, show the first line of examples where $f(x) = x + 2$. Uncover the second line of function machines where $f(x) = 3x - 2$ and ask students for the values of y (the output). Using the third line of function machines, guide students to develop the function rule $f(x) = 2x$ given the values in the table.

Play the *Function Machine Game* as follows. Player A thinks of a rule and acts as a function machine to compute a new number y from x given to them. (Record x and y on the chart for each computation.) When a student wishes to guess the rule, they must first give an example for x and y. If correct, they may give the rule and write the equation. The winner of each round becomes player A and the game continues.

Use the Algebra Activity worksheet for guided practice for group or individual instruction. After the students have completed the worksheet, discuss the answers.

Answers

1. $y = 3x$

2. $y = 0.5x$

3. $y = x + 4$

4. $y = -x$

Using Overhead Manipulatives

(Use with Algebra 1, Lesson 4-3)

Relations

Objective Model a relation and its inverse.

Materials
- overhead geoboard*
- geobands*

* = available in Overhead Manipulative Resources

Demonstration
Using Geoboards for Modeling Relations and Inverses

- Use a geoboard to construct a triangle with vertices at (2, 2), (3, 5), (5, 1) shown to the right.

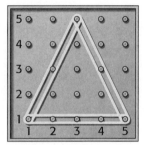

- Ask students to name the points in the interior of the triangle. **(2, 2), (3, 2), (3, 3), (3, 4), (4, 2)**

- Tell students that the set of points is a relation. Then tell them that the **domain** of a relation is the set of all first coordinates from the ordered pairs. Ask them to state the domain of the relation. **(2, 3, 4)** Inform students that the **range** of a relation is the set of all second coordinates of the ordered pairs. Have them state the range of the relation. **(2, 3, 4)**

- Tell students that the **inverse** of any relation is obtained by switching the coordinates in each ordered pair of the relation. Have them list the ordered pairs for the inverse relation. **(2, 2), (2, 3), (3, 3), (4, 3), (2, 4)**

- On the geoboard, construct a triangle containing interior points corresponding to the inverse relation. **See answer to the right.**

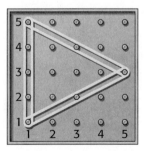

Extension
Comparing a Relation and Its Inverse

- Repeat the activity above for a rectangle with vertices (1, 1), (5, 1), (5, 3), and (1, 3) and a triangle with vertices (1, 1), (5, 1), and (1, 4). Have students compare the size and shape of the two rectangles and their position. **The figures have the same size and shape, but are in different positions.**
Ask students to compare the size and shape of the two triangles and their position. **The figures have the same size and shape, and are in the same position.**
Point out that the relation and its inverse are equivalent when they are the same size and shape and are in the same position.

- Have students suggest figures to build on the geoboard. Ask them to name the interior points and try to predict the figure corresponding to the inverse of the relation. **Answers will vary.**

Algebra Activity Recording Sheet

(Use with the activity on page 207 in Lesson 4-3 of the Student Edition.)

Relations and Inverses

Materials: colored pencils

Analyze the Data

1. What do you notice about the location of the points you graphed when you looked at the folded paper?

2. Unfold the paper. Describe the transformation of each point and its inverse.

3. What do you think are the ordered pairs that represent the points on the fold line? Describe these in terms of x and y.

Make a Conjecture

4. How could you graph the inverse of a function without writing ordered pairs first?

 Teaching Algebra with Manipulatives

Using Overhead Manipulatives

(Use with Algebra 1, Lesson 4-5)

Graphing Linear Relations

> **Objective** Graphing linear equations on a coordinate plane.
>
> **Materials**
> - coordinate grid transparency*
> - transparency pen*
> - transparency prepared as described below
>   three blank transparencies * = available in Overhead Manipulative Resources

Demonstration
Graphing Linear Equations

- Prepare a transparency with the table shown at the right. Do not copy the numbers shown in parentheses or the heading of the second column.
- Place a blank transparency on the table transparency. Have students complete the table to find five solutions for the equation $y = x + 1$.
- Have students graph all of the ordered pairs. Ask them whether the graph appears to be linear. **yes** Have them draw a line through the points.

x	(x + 1)	y	(x, y)
−2	(−2 + 1)	(−1)	(−2, −1)
−1	(−1 + 1)	(0)	(−1, 0)
0	(0 + 1)	(1)	(0, 1)
1	(1 + 1)	(2)	(1, 2)
2	(2 + 1)	(3)	(2, 3)

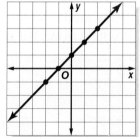

- Place a blank transparency on the table transparency. Have students complete the table to find five solutions for the equation $y = -3x$. **(−2, 6), (−1, 3), (0, 0), (1, −3), (2, −6)**
- Have students graph all of the ordered pairs and draw a line through the points.

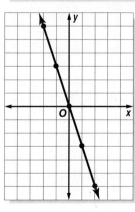

- Place a blank transparency on the table transparency. Write the equation $3x + 4y = 6$ above the table. Ask students how to solve this equation for y. **Subtract 3x from each side; divide each side by 4.**

- Write $\frac{6 - 3x}{4}$ in the second column of the table.

  Continue with activity as above.

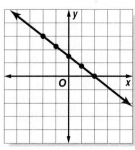

Algebra 1—Chapter 4

Using Overhead Manipulatives

(Use with Algebra 1, Lesson 4-6)

Functions

Objective Determine whether a relation is a function.

Materials
- overhead geoboard and geobands*
- transparency pens*
- dot paper transparency*

* = available in Overhead Manipulative Resources

Demonstration
Is the Relation a Function?

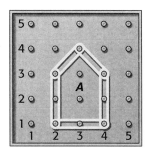

- Form a polygon on the geoboard as shown at the right. Ask students to find the area of the polygon. **5 square units**

- Copy the polygon on the dot paper transparency and label A. Write the ordered pair (A, 5) next to the figure. Ask students what the ordered pair represents. **the relation that maps the polygon to its area.**

- Form each of the polygons shown below. For each polygon, copy on dot paper and ask students to name an ordered pair representing the figure. **(B, 3.5), (C, 8), (D, 9), (E, 9)**

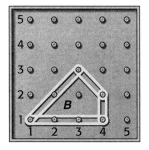 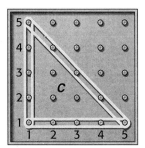 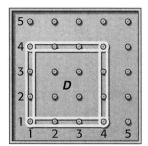 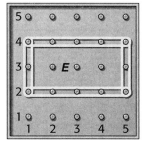

- Ask students to describe the relation that maps each polygon to its area. **(A, 5), (B, 3.5), (C, 8), (D, 9), (E, 8)**

- Ask whether it is true that for each polygon there is exactly one area. **yes** Explain that this type of relation is called a **function.**

- Ask students to state the relation mapping the area of each polygon to itself. **{(5, A), (3.5, B), (8, C), (9, D), (8, E)}** Write the relation on the transparency. Ask whether each area corresponds to exactly one polygon. **no**

- Ask whether the relation mapping the area of each polygon to itself is a function and why. **No; the same range element is paired with more than one domain element, or different polygons can have the same area.**

- Ask students to use any combination of the figures to state a relation that maps the area of the polygon to itself so that the relation is a function. **Sample answer: {(5, A), (3.5, B), (8, C), (9, D)}**

 Teaching Algebra with Manipulatives

Mini-Project

(Use with Algebra 1, Lesson 4-6)

Functions or Not?

Work in pairs. You will need one red die, one green die, graph paper, and a ruler.

Roll each die four times to complete the chart. Write the result as ordered pairs.

Red	Green

Plot the ordered pairs on the grid below.

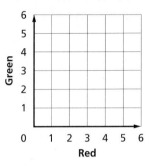

Use the information above to answer the following questions.

1. What is the relation? Write as a set of ordered pairs.

2. What is the domain of the relation?

3. What is the range of the relation?

4. The **vertical line test** for a function states that if any vertical line passes through no more than one point of the graph of a relation, then the relation is a function. Does the vertical line test indicate that this relation is a function?

5. Repeat the experiment three times. Answer the questions for each experiment. Can you make any generalizations about the results?

Algebra 1—Chapter 4

Algebra Activity Recording Sheet

(Use with the activity on page 241 in Lesson 4-8 of the Student Edition.)

Looking for Patterns

Materials: scissors, several pieces of string

Analyze the Data

1. Describe the pattern and write a sequence that describes the number of loops and the number of pieces of string.

2. Write an expression that you could use to find the number of pieces of string you would have if you made n loops.

3. How many pieces of string would you have if you made 20 loops?

90   *Teaching Algebra with Manipulatives*

Algebra Activity Transparency Master
(Use with Algebra 1, Lesson 4-8)

Functions

x	y

Function Machine

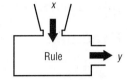

x	y
5	7
1	3
10	12

$f(x) = x + 2$

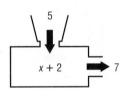

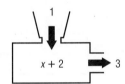

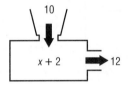

x	y
1	
0	
3	

$f(x) = 3x - 2$

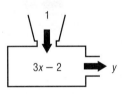

x	y
4	8
−1	−2
3	6

$f(x) = ?$

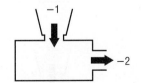

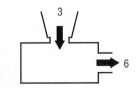

Teaching Algebra with Manipulatives

Algebra 1—Chapter 4

Algebra Activity
(Use with Algebra 1, Lesson 4-8)

Functions

Find the rule for each function machine.

Example:

x	y
4	3
7	6
0	−1
−2	−3

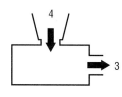 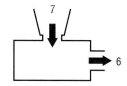 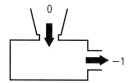 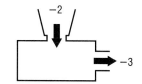

$y = x - 1$

1.

x	y

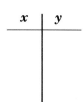 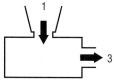 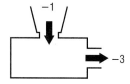 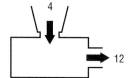

_____

2.

x	y

 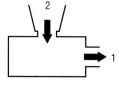 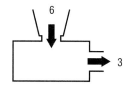 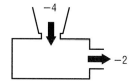 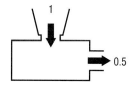

_____

3.

x	y

 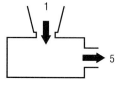 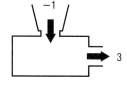 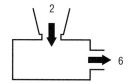 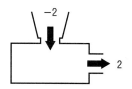

_____

4.

x	y

 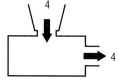 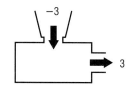 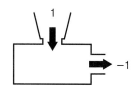 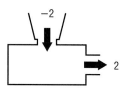

_____

5 Analyzing Linear Equations
Teaching Notes and Overview

Using Overhead Manipulatives

Slope
(pp. 96–97 of this booklet)

Use With Lesson 5-1.

Objective Find the slope of a line.

Materials
coordinate grid transparency*
transparency pens*
straightedge*
blank transparencies
* = available in Overhead Manipulative Resources

This demonstration contains two activities.

• Demonstration 1 develops the meaning of the slope of a line. On a grid, students graph and label two points, and draw the line determined by the points. Next, they find the slope of the line by finding the rise and run.

• Demonstration 2 investigates the slope of lines parallel to the *x*-axis and the slope of lines parallel to the *y*-axis. Students use what they learned in Demonstration 1 to find these slopes.

Answers
Answers appear on the teacher demonstration instructions on pages 96–97.

Algebra Activity Recording Sheet

Investigating Slope-Intercept Form
(p. 98 of this booklet)

Use With Lesson 5-3 as a preview activity. This corresponds to the activity on page 271 in the Student Edition.

Objective Model real-world data with an equation in slope-intercept form.

Materials
scissors
plastic sandwich bag
long rubber band
tape

centimeter ruler
washers
grid paper

You may want to use student pairs to do this activity or do it as a classroom demonstration with student participation. If you decide to do the activity as a classroom demonstration, make the model ahead of time. Then have students perform the experiment and collect the data. Analyzing the data and making a conjecture can be done in small groups.

Some students may be interested in investigating this concept in greater depth. From the study of physics, this relationship between force (washers) and the deformation of the spring (rubber band) is called Hooke's Law. Have students or student pairs write a short report and present it to the class.

Answers
See Teacher Wraparound Edition p. 271.

Using Overhead Manipulatives

Slope-Intercept Form of Linear Equations
(p. 99 of this booklet)

Use With Lesson 5-3.

Objective Write linear equations in slope-intercept form.

Materials
coordinate grid transparency*
transparency pen*
blank transparencies
* = available in Overhead Manipulative Resources

The demonstration contains activities in which students identify the slope and *y*-intercept of a line. Also, they write the equation of a line by using the slope and *y*-intercept or a point on the *y*-axis.

Answers
Answers appear on the teacher demonstration instructions on page 99.

Using Overhead Manipulatives

Point-Slope and Standard Form of Equations
(pp. 100–101 of this booklet)

Use With Lesson 5-5.

Objective Write linear equations in point-slope and standard forms.

This demonstration contains two activities.

- Demonstration 1 shows the graph of a line with a point S. Using the graph, students are asked to find the slope of the line. The coordinates of a known point and the slope of the line are used to write the equation of the line in point-slope form. Rewriting the point-slope form into standard form is covered. The process is repeated for another point on the graph.

- Demonstration 2 shows a graph of a line that passes through the origin. Students are asked to write an equation of the line in point-slope form and standard form.

Answers
Answers appear on the teacher demonstration instructions on pages 100–101.

Algebra Activity

Slopes of Parallel and Perpendicular Lines
(pp. 102–103 of this booklet)

Use With Lesson 5-6 as a preview activity.

Objective Discover the relationship between slopes of parallel lines and slopes of perpendicular lines.

Materials
centimeter grid paper transparency*
parallel and perpendicular lines transparency*
(p. 103)
tracing paper
graph paper
* = available in Overhead Manipulative Resources

Students find the slopes and y-intercepts of the lines a and b shown on a transparency. The centimeter grid paper and parallel/perpendicular lines transparencies follow this teacher demonstration for Lesson 5-6. The Algebra Activity worksheet follows the latter. They work in groups to complete Exercises 1 and 2 on the Algebra Activity worksheet. Have students complete Exercises 3 and 4. Discuss the relationship of slopes of parallel lines. Next, students find the slopes of lines c and d shown on the overhead. Again they work in groups to complete Exercises 5 through 8 on the Algebra Activity worksheet. Discuss the relationship of slopes of perpendicular lines.

Answers

1. Students trace and cut out Figure 1.

2. Answers will vary.

3. The slopes are the same and the y-intercepts are different.

4. Answers will depend on Exercise 1.

5. Students trace and cut out Figure 2.

6. Answers will vary.

7. The product of their slopes is -1 or one slope is the negative reciprocal of the other. The y-intercepts are different.

8. Answers will depend on Exercise 5.

Algebra Activity Recording Sheet

Perpendicular Lines
(p. 104 of this booklet)

Use With the activity on page 293 in Lesson 5-6 of the Student Edition.

Objective Discover the relationship between slopes of perpendicular lines.

Carefully review the directions for Steps 1 and 2. Next, ask students to read exercises 1 through 9. Some students may need clarification as to the meaning of rotation.

You may want to form groups of two or three students to do this activity. Have each group follow the directions for Steps 1 and 2. Allow enough time for each group to complete Collecting the Data, Exercises 1–5, and Analyzing the Data, Exercises 6–8. Have each group report their findings on Exercises 1–5. Then do the same for Exercises 6–8. Discuss exercise 9. Ask students to distinguish between the slopes of perpendicular and parallel lines.

Answers
See Teacher Wraparound Edition p. 293.

Algebra Activity Recording Sheet

Making Predictions
(p. 105 of this booklet)

Use With the activity on page 299 in Lesson 5-7 of the Student Edition.

Objective Make a scatter plot and interpret points on the plot.

Materials
cloth tape measure or metersticks
centimeter grid paper

Familiarize students with the step-by-step process outlined on the Activity sheet. Students work in pairs to discover the relationship between the lengths of their feet and their heights. You may wish to give students copies of the class scatter plot and ask each group to draw a line of best-fit. Then have the groups compare their lines and equations. Do all lines render the same prediction for a foot length of 25 centimeters? Also, you may want them to experiment with other pairs of data and make conjectures.

Answers
See Teacher Wraparound Edition p. 299.

Using Overhead Manipulatives

Scatter Plots
(p. 106 of this booklet)

Use with Lesson 5-7.

Objective Interpret points on a scatter plot.

Materials
cloth tape measure
lined paper transparency*
centimeter grid transparency*
transparency pens*
projectible graphing calculator, if available
* = available in Overhead Manipulative Resources

The demonstration is a measuring activity involving the circumference of the students' heads and their height. The ordered pair for each student is plotted on a grid transparency. The scatter plot is then analyzed to determine the relationship. That is, if it is positive, negative, or has no correlation.

Answers
Answers appear on the teacher demonstration instructions on page 106.

Mini-Project

Scatter Plots
(p. 107 of this booklet)

Use With Lesson 5-7.

Objectives Interpret points on a scatter plot. Write equations for best-fit lines.

This activity requires students to work in groups of two or three to plot data from a chart on a grid. The groups determine the line of best fit and write the equation for it. Then they are asked to make predictions.

Answers

1. See students' graphs.

2. See students' graphs.

3. Sample answer: $3x - 4y = -52$

4. Sample prediction: 21.50 m

5. Sample prediction: 2008

6. Sample prediction: 2.29 m

7. The Soviet Union and its allies boycotted the Olympics in 1984. In view of the dominance of the event by this group in previous Olympics, the best athletes did not compete in 1984.

Using Overhead Manipulatives

(Use with Algebra 1, Lesson 5-1)

Find the Slope of a Line

Objective Find the slope of a line.

Materials
- coordinate grid transparency*
- transparency pens*
- straightedge*
- blank transparencies

* = available in Overhead Manipulative Resources

Demonstration 1
Finding Slope: Positive, Negative

- At the right, copy Graph 1 on the coordinate grid transparency.

- Tell students that slope is defined as $\dfrac{\textbf{change in } y}{\textbf{change in } x}$ or $\dfrac{\textbf{rise}}{\textbf{run}}$.

  Ask them what the rise and run are for this line. **(3; 2)** Ask why the values are both positive. **Movements up and right are denoted by positive numbers; movements down and left are denoted by negative numbers.**

- Ask students to find the slope of the line. $\dfrac{3}{2}$

- Ask whether moving up 3 units and right 2 units from $(3, 5)$ will result in a point on the line. **yes**

- Graph and label the points $C(0, 0)$ and $D(-1, -4)$ on the second coordinate grid. Draw the line determined by the points.

- Ask students to find the rise and run for the line in graph 2. **4; 1**

  "What is the slope of the line?" $\dfrac{4}{1}$ **or 4**

- Ask, "Does it matter which point is used first when finding slope?" **no, as long as its coordinates are used first to calculate both rise and run**

- Write $\dfrac{0 - (-4)}{0 - (-1)} = \dfrac{4}{1} = 4$ and $\dfrac{4 - 0}{-1 - 0} = \dfrac{-4}{-1} = 4$ beside the grid to show students this is true.

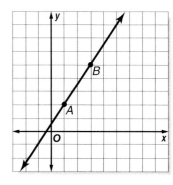

Graph 1

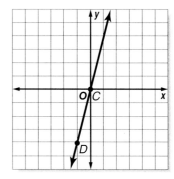

Graph 2

Demonstration 2
Finding Slope: Zero, Undefined

• Place a coordinate grid transparency on the screen.
• Ask students how to graph the line $y = -3$. **Graph a line through all points where $y = -3$; the line will be parallel to the x-axis.** Graph $y = -3$.
• Ask students to name two points on the line. **Answers will vary.**
• Have students find the slope of the line. **0**
• Ask whether the slope would be different for any other line parallel to the x-axis. **no**

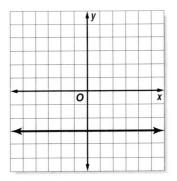

• Ask students how to graph the line $x = 2$. **Graph a line through all points where $x = 2$; the line will be parallel to the y-axis.** Graph $x = 2$.
• Ask students to name two points on the line. **Answers will vary.**
• Ask students to find the slope of the line. **The slope of the line $x = 2$ is undefined.**
• Ask whether the slope would be undefined for any line parallel to the y-axis and why. **Yes; since the value of x is constant, the change in x will be 0 for any value of x.**

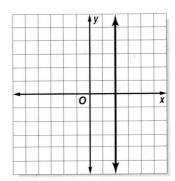

Algebra Activity Recording Sheet

(Use with the Lesson 5-3 Preview Activity on page 271 in the Student Edition.)

Investigating Slope-Intercept Form

Materials: scissors, plastic sandwich bag, long rubber band, tape, centimeter ruler, washers, grid paper

Analyze the Data

1. The domain contains values represented by the independent variable, washers. The range contains values represented by the dependent variable, distance. On **grid paper**, graph the ordered pairs (washers, distance).

2. Write a sentence that describes the points on the graph.

3. Describe the point that represents the trial with no washers in the bag.

4. The rate of change can be found by using the formula for slope.

$$\frac{\text{rise}}{\text{run}} = \frac{\text{change in distance}}{\text{change in number of washers}}$$

Find the rate of change in the distance from the desktop to the end of the bag as more washers are added.

5. Explain how the rate of change is shown on the graph.

Make a Conjecture

For Exercises 6–8, draw your graphs on grid paper.

Using Overhead Manipulatives

(Use with Algebra 1, Lesson 5-3)

Slope-Intercept Form of Linear Equations

Objective Write linear equations in slope-intercept form.

Materials
- coordinate grid transparency*
- transparency pen*
- blank transparencies
* = available in Overhead Manipulative Resources

Demonstration

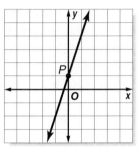

- Copy the graph shown at the right.
- Tell students that you want to write an equation for the line. Ask them to name the coordinate of *P*. **0, 1** Then ask them to find the slope of the line. **3**
- Write $y = mx + b$ on a blank transparency. Tell students that this is the slope-intercept form. Ask students what *m* represents. **slope** What *b* represents. **y-intercept** Ask what you know about the line from this equation. **The line crosses the y-axis at 1 and has a slope of 3.**
- Have students write an equation for a line that has a slope of 3 and a *y*-intercept of 1. **$y = 3x + 1$**
- Show the following graphs and ask the students to state the slope and the *y*-intercept. Then have them write the slope-intercept form for each line.

1.

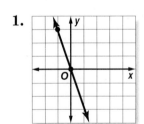

$y = -3x$

2.

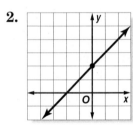

$y = x + 2$

3.

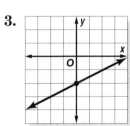

$y = \frac{1}{2}x - 2$

99

Using Overhead Manipulatives
(Use with Algebra 1, Lesson 5-5)

Linear Equations in Point-Slope and Standard Forms

Objective Write linear equations in point-slope and standard forms.

Materials
- coordinate grid transparency*
- transparency pen*
- blank transparencies

* = available in Overhead Manipulative Resources

Demonstration 1
Writing an Equation of a Line

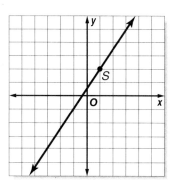

- Copy the graph shown at the right on the coordinate grid transparency.
- Tell students that you want to write an equation for the line. Ask them to name the coordinates of S. **1,2** Then ask them to find the slope of the line. $\dfrac{3}{2}$
- Write $\dfrac{y_2 - y_1}{x_2 - x_1} = m$ on a blank transparency.

  Substitute the coordinates of S for x_1 and y_1, and $\dfrac{3}{2}$ for m.

  Ask students to simplify the equation so it is in the form $y - y_1 = m(x - x_1)$.

  Substitute (x, y) for (x_2, y_2); $\dfrac{y - y_1}{x - x_1} = m$.

  Multiply each side by $(x - x_1)$; $y - y_1 = m(x - x_1)$. $\mathbf{(y - 2) = \dfrac{3}{2}(x - 1)}$

- Tell students that this is the **point-slope** form of a linear equation. Ask what you know about the line from this form of the equation. **the coordinates of one point on the line and the slope of the line**

- Remind students that the **standard form** of a line is in the form $Ax + By = C$ where A, B and C are real numbers and A and B are not both zero. (Usually A and B are integers and $A \geq 0$.) Show them how to write the equation of the line in standard form. Multiply each side by 2; use the distributive property; subtract $3x$ from each side; add 4 to each side; multiply by -1; the standard form is $3x - 2y = -1$.

- Have students repeat the process using a different point on the line. Ask whether the same equation results from using the coordinates of any point on the line. **yes**

Demonstration 2
Writing an Equation of a Line

- Display this graph on a second coordinate grid transparency.
- Ask students to name the coordinates of *M* and *N*. **(0, 0), (1, 4)**
- Ask students how to find the slope of the line from the coordinates of these two points. **by dividing the change in *y* by the change in *x***
- Write the formula for the point-slope form of a linear equation on the blank transparency.

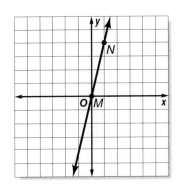

$$y - y_1 = m(x - x_1)$$

Substitute the slope and the coordinates of *M* in the equation. Have students tell how to simplify the equation and write it in standard form. **4*x* − *y* = 0**

- Have students substitute the coordinates of *N* in the slope-intercept form. Ask whether the same equation results from using the coordinates of *M, N,* or any point on the line. **yes**

- Ask students to name a different point on the line. **Answers will vary.** Have students show that the point is on the line.

Algebra Activity
(Use with Algebra 1, Lesson 5-6)

Slopes of Parallel and Perpendicular Lines

Materials: tracing paper, scissors

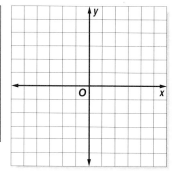

Activity 1
Parallel Lines

Collect the Data
1. Trace Figure 1 on tracing paper and cut it out.

2. Place parallel lines a and b on the coordinate graph in three different positions. For each position, record the slope and y-intercept of lines a and b in the chart below.

Analyze the Data
3. What similarities do you find between lines a and b?

4. Write an equation for each line using the slope-intercept form.

	Slope of line c	y-intercept of line c	Slope of line d	y-intercept of line d	Equation of line c	Equation of line d
1						
2						
3						

Activity 2
Perpendicular Lines

Collect the Data
5. Trace Figure 2 on tracing paper and cut it out.

6. Place perpendicular lines c and d on the coordinate graph in three different positions. For each position, record the slope and y-intercept of lines c and d in the chart below.

Analyze the Data
7. What similarities do you find between lines c and d?

8. Write an equation for each line using the slope-intercept form.

	Slope of line a	y-intercept of line a	Slope of line b	y-intercept of line b	Equation of line a	Equation of line b
1						
2						
3						

NAME _____ DATE _____ PERIOD _____

Algebra Activity Transparency Master

(Use with Algebra 1, Lesson 5-6)

Slopes of Parallel and Perpendicular Lines

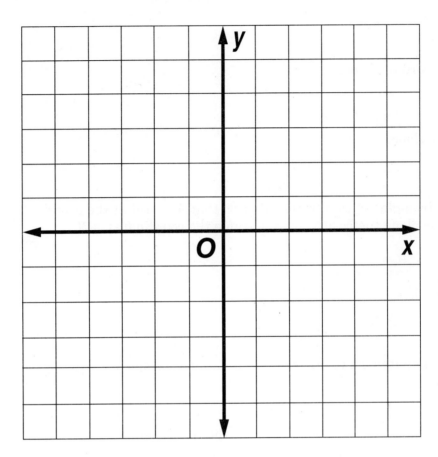

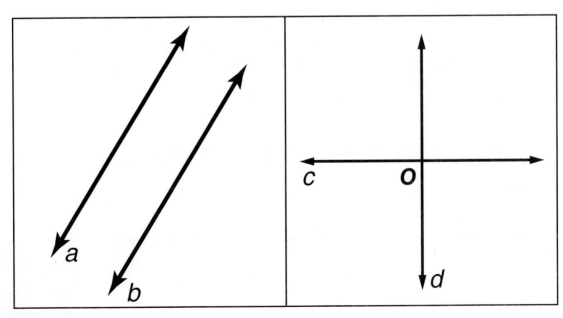

103

Algebra Activity Recording Sheet

(Use with the activity on page 293 in Lesson 5-6 of the Student Edition.)

Perpendicular Lines

Materials: scissors, grid paper

Analyze

1. Name the coordinates of *B*.

2. What is the slope of side *c*?

3. Rotate the triangle 90° counterclockwise so that *A* is still at the origin and side *b* is along the positive *y*-axis. Name the coordinates of *B*.

4. What is the slope of side *c*?

5. Repeat the activity for two other different scalene triangles.

6. For each triangle and its rotation, what is the relationship between the first position of side *c* and the second?

7. For each triangle and its rotation, describe the relationship between the coordinates of *B* in the first and second positions.

8. Describe the relationship between the slopes of *c* in each position.

Make a Conjecture

9. Describe the relationship between the slopes of any two perpendicular lines.

Algebra Activity Recording Sheet

(Use with the activity on page 299 in Lesson 5-7 of the Student Edition.)

Making Predictions

Materials: meterstick, grid paper

Analyze the Data

1. Is there a correlation between foot length and height for the members of your class? If so, describe it.

2. Draw a line that summarizes the data and shows how the height changes as the foot length changes.

Make a Conjecture

3. Use the line to predict the height of a person whose foot length is 25 centimeters. Explain your method.

Using Overhead Manipulatives

(Use with Algebra 1, Lesson 5-7)

Scatter Plots

Objective Interpret points on a scatter plot.

Materials
- cloth tape measure
- lined paper transparency*
- centimeter grid transparency*
- transparency pens*

* = available in Overhead Manipulative Resources

Demonstration

- On a lined paper transparency, prepare a three-column chart with the headings Name, Circumference, and Height.

- Attach a cloth measuring tape to a wall so that it can be used for measuring height. Have a student stand against the wall. Measure the students height in inches and record it in the chart on the lined transparency.
Sample answer: 68 in.

- Use another measuring tape to measure the circumference of the student's head in inches. Record this measure. **Sample answer: 22 in.**

- Tell students, "You will organize this data using the ordered pair (circumference, height)." Ask them to name the ordered pair for this student.
Sample answer: (22, 68)

- On the centimeter grid transparency, prepare a graph like the one above. Review plotting ordered pairs and plot the sample ordered pair on the graph.

- Find the ordered pair for each student and plot the data on the graph or have students complete the scatter plot at their seats.

- Ask students whether there appears to be a correlation between head circumference and height. **positive correlation** You may want to review the meaning of positive, negative and no correlation as shown on pages 296–297 in the Student Edition. Also, ask students if they see any other relationships. **Sample answer: Height is about 3 times the circumference.**

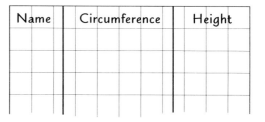

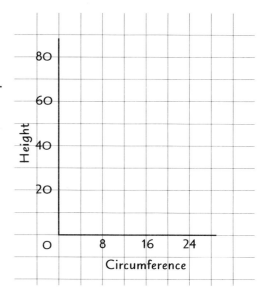

Mini-Project

(Use with Algebra 1, Lesson 5-7)

Scatter Plots

Work in small groups to solve the
following problems about the Summer
Olympic Games. The Games are held
every four years. The women's shot put
was introduced as an Olympic event in
1948. Listed at the right are the gold
medalists and their winning distances.

Year	Winner	Distance (in meters)
1948	Ostermeyer (France)	13.75
1952	Zybina (U.S.S.R)	15.28
1956	Tishkyevich (U.S.S.R)	16.59
1960	Press (U.S.S.R)	17.32
1964	Press (U.S.S.R)	18.14
1968	Gummel (East Germany)	19.61
1972	Chizhova (U.S.S.R)	21.03
1976	Christova (Bulgaria)	21.16
1980	Sluplanek (East Germany)	22.41
1984	Losch (West Germany)	20.48
1988	Lisovskaya (U.S.S.R)	22.24
1992	Kriveleva (Unified Team)	21.07
1996	Kumbernuss (Germany)	20.57
2000	Karolchik (Belarus)	20.57

Source: Yahoo Sports

1. Plot the data in the coordinate plane
   provided.

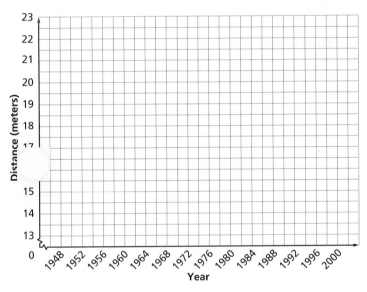

2. Draw a single straight line that you think best represents the data.
   The number of points above your line should be about the same as
   the number of the points below the line. This line is called the "line of
   best fit."

3. Use two points from your line of best fit to find the equation of the line.

4. Predict the winning distance in the year 2004.

5. Predict when the winning distance will be more than 25 meters.

6. Predict when the winning distance would have been had the women's
   shot put been an event in the 1908 Olympics.

7. The winner of the women's shot put in 1984 was Losch (West
   Germany). Her distance was 20.48 meters. Do some research to find
   why the winning distance might have been so short in 1984.

6

Solving Linear Inequalities
Teaching Notes and Overview

Using Overhead Manipulatives

Solving Inequalities Using Addition and Subtraction
(pp. 111–113 of this booklet)

Use With Lesson 6-1.

Objective Model and solve inequalities using addition and subtraction.

Materials
inequality mat transparency*
overhead counters*
equation mat transparency*
number line transparency*
transparency pen*
two blank transparencies prepared as described for the activity
* = available in Overhead Manipulative Resources

There are two demonstrations and one extension.

- Demonstration 1 involves using the Addition and Subtraction Properties for Inequality found in the Student Edition. It is important that students know how to use these properties. Displaying the properties using transparencies, as well as referencing them in the text, are beneficial to the visual learners in the class. After using the inequality mat to develop the solution to $4 + x > -2$, write the solution set on the transparency. Make sure students understand how to read the solution set and what it means.

  Ask students several questions about the set to check their understanding. For example, "Is -6, a member of the set? Explain." **No, the member must be greater than 6.** Some students may find it helpful to see another similar type of inequality developed and solved with the mat transparency. Use the same process for finding the solution set of $2x + 3 < 3x - 7$.

- Demonstration 2 deals with translating a sentence containing an inequality phrase into mathematical symbols. Then the mat transparency is used to solve it. Once again, using a transparency to display the inequality

chart, as well as pointing them out in the text, are needed to assist the visual learners.

- The Extension involves graphing the three solution sets developed in the two demonstrations.

Answers
Answers appear on the teacher demonstration instructions on pages 111–113.

Mini-Project

Multiplying Inequalities by −1
(p. 114 of this booklet)

Use With Lesson 6-1.

Objective Multiplying inequalities by -1.

This project requires students to work with a partner. They are asked to read and understand the three examples, and then do exercises that check on their understanding. It is essential that students know that when an inequality is multiplied by -1, the sense of the inequality must change.

Answers

1. $x < -2$
2. $x > -5$
3. $-x > -6$
4. $-x < 7$
5. $x > 4$
6. $x < 8$
7. $-x > 10$
8. $x > 0$
9. $>; <$
10. The direction of the inequality symbol must be reversed.

Algebra Activity Recording Sheet

Solving Inequalities
(p. 115 of this booklet)

Use With Lesson 6-2 as a preview activity. This corresponds to the activity on page 324 in the Student Edition.

Objective Solving inequalities.

Materials
algebra tiles

Equation mats are used for this activity. Students utilize the mats to solve four inequalities. For guided practice, you may want to use the mats to solve similar inequalities. Have students explain in their own words how they used the mat to solve each one of the inequalities. Encourage students to answer questions proposed by other students about their solutions.

Answers
See Teacher Wraparound Edition p. 324.

Algebra Activity
Compound Inequalities
(pp. 116–118 of this booklet)

Use With Lesson 6-4.

Objective Solving compound inequalities.

Materials
Each pair of students needs the following:
scissors
yellow and blue permanent highlighting pens
copy of this Algebra Activity sheet
transparency on compound inequalities
worksheet for graphing compound inequalities

It is suggested that students work in groups of two to do this activity on solving compound inequalities. It involves a direction sheet with Exercises 1–9; a transparency with seven number lines; and a worksheet with Exercises 1–4. Make sure students understand the purpose of the copy of this Algebra Activity sheet, transparency on compound inequalities, and the worksheet for graphing compound inequalities. Students use highlighting pens to show the graph of $x \leq 3$, and then $x > -2$ on transparencies. Then they cut them out. These are used to find the solution sets for Exercises 5–6.

Using these as models, students place each graph on the same number line. They align the origins from each graph. Students find out that the *and* yields a green and that the *or* a yellow, blue or green. Have students share how they described the solution sets in their own words.

Answers
1–4. See student's work.

5. $\{x | -2 < x \leq 3\}$

6. $\{x | x \text{ is a real number}\}$

7. Answers will vary.

8. See student's work.

9. Answers will vary.

Answers to Activity Worksheet

1. Sample answer: the real numbers greater than -3 and less than 2

2. Sample answer: the real numbers greater than 0 and less than 5

3. Sample answer: the real numbers

4. Sample answer: the real numbers greater than -3

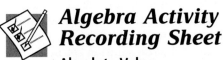

Algebra Activity Recording Sheet
Absolute Value
(p. 119 of this booklet)

Use With the activity on page 347 in Lesson 6-5 of the Student Edition.

Objective Modeling absolute value.

Materials
timer or clock with a second hand

This Algebra Activity explores an inequality of the form $|x| > n$. Students work in pairs on this activity about absolute value. If you have an odd number of students, one student could record the data for the class. If not, a volunteer could do the job. You will need to monitor their work. Discuss the findings as soon as all pairs have completed the activity. Some pairs may need assistance.

Answers
See Teacher Wraparound Edition p. 347.

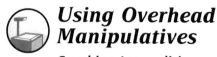

Using Overhead Manipulatives

Graphing Inequalities
(pp. 120–121 of this booklet)

Use With Lesson 6-6.

Objective Graph a linear inequality and describe the graph of the inequality.

Materials
coordinate grid transparency*
transparency pens*
blank transparencies prepared
as described below
* = available in Overhead Manipulative Resources

This demonstration contains two parts.

- Demonstration 1 deals with graphing $y > 2$ and $y < x + 2$ in the coordinate system. The solution set for each inequality is given. Dashed lines are used to show that the points on the line are not in the solution set. Ask students to describe the solution set in their own words.

- Demonstration 2 shows the graph of $y \geq 3x - 5$. Make sure students know that the points on the line for $y = 3x - 5$ are part of the solution set along with all of the points above the line. Again have students describe the solution set in their own words. Next, students are asked to describe the solution sets of three more inequalities. In the next three problems, a description of a solution set is given in words. Then students are asked to write the inequality that matches the description. There are three of these to complete.

Answers
Answers appear on the teacher demonstration instructions on pages 120–121.

Using Overhead Manipulatives

(Use with Algebra 1, Lesson 6-1)

Solving Inequalities Using Addition and Subtraction

> **Objective** Model and solve inequalities using addition and subtraction
>
> **Materials**
> - inequality map transparency*
> - overhead counters*
> - equation mat transparency*
> - number line transparency*
> - transparency pen*
> - two blank transparencies prepared
> - as described for the activity
> * = available in Overhead Manipulative Resources

Demonstration 1
Solving Inequalities Using Addition and Subtraction

- On the top half of a blank transparency, write the Addition and Subtraction Properties for Inequality found on pages 318–319 of the Student Edition. On the bottom half, copy the inequalities chart found on page 320. You will use this transparency in the demonstrations.

- Place the inequality mat transparency on the screen with the left side down. Tell students that this represents an unbalanced scale. Remind students that a cup represents a variable, a counter with a positive sign represents a positive integer and a counter with a negative sign represents a negative integer. Place 4 positive counters and a cup to the left of the triangle, and 2 negative counters to the right.

- Tell students that since the left side is down, it is heavier and represents the greater value. Ask them what inequality is modeled. **4 + *x* > −2** Write the inequality at the base of the mat.

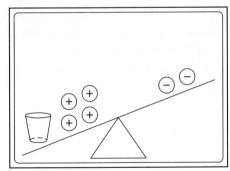

$4 + x > -2$

- Inform students that to solve this inequality, you must find the least number of counters in the cup that results in a true sentence. One way to do this is by guess-and-check. Place 1 positive counter in the cup and ask whether a true sentence results. **yes** Remove the counter. Ask whether zero counters result in a true sentence. **yes** Repeat for −1, −4, and −6. **yes; yes; no**

- Remind students that the inequality states that the left side must be *greater than* the right side. Since −6 results in both sides having the same value, than the value of *x* must be *greater than* −6. Write *x* > −6. Ask whether there is an upper limit on the value of *x*. **no**

- Show students the transparency with the properties for inequalities. Explain that these properties can be used to solve inequalities. Be sure that students are comfortable with the properties.
- Place the mat on the screen again and model the original inequality $4 + x > -2$.
- Ask what you should do to be able to remove all counters from the left side. **Place 4 zero pairs on the right side.** Place the zero pairs on the right. Then remove 4 positive counters from each side. Ask students to state the solution. **$\{x|x > -6\}$** Have them compare this to the result of substituting values for x. **They are the same.**

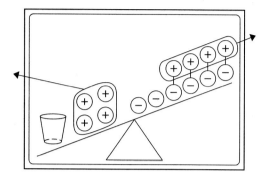

- Flip the inequality mat so that the left side is up. Write $2x + 3 < 3x - 7$. Ask students which side of the inequality represents the greater value. **right side** Point out that this matches the way the scale is shown.
- Ask students how to model each side of the inequality. **2 cups and 3 positive counters on the end that is up, 3 cups and 7 negative counters on the end that is down.**
- Ask students how to solve the inequality. **Remove 2 cups from each side; add 7 zero pairs to the right side; remove 7 negative counters from each side; the solution is $\{x|10 > x\}$ or $\{x|x > 10\}$.**
- Show students how to check the solution by mentally substituting numbers greater and less than 10 for the cups.

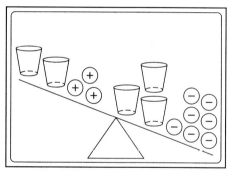

$$2x + 3 < 3x - 7$$

Demonstration 2
Solving Inequalities Using Addition and Subtraction

- Use the transparency you prepared with the chart on page 320 of the Student Edition to review the inequality symbols and their meanings.

$$2x + 3 < 3x - 7$$

- Display the equation mat transparency. Across the top of the mat, write *4 less than twice a number is no more than the number plus 1*. Ask students what inequality symbol you need? ≤ Write the symbol in the center of the mat by altering the equals sign.

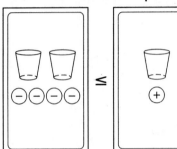

4 less than twice a number is no more than the number plus one

- Model each side of the inequality from the written form.

- Ask students how to solve the inequality. **Remove a cup from each side; add 4 zero pairs to the right side; remove 4 negative counters from each side; the solution is $\{x \mid x \le 5\}$.**

- Check the solution by substituting 5 counters for each cup, then 4, then 6.

Extension
Graphing Solutions to Inequalities

Use the number line transparency to graph the solutions to the inequalities solved in Teacher Demonstrations 1 and 2.

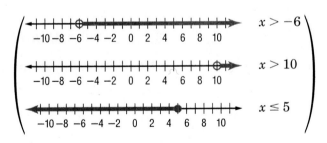

$x > -6$

$x > 10$

$x \le 5$

Algebra 1—Chapter 6

Mini-Project

(Use with Algebra 1, Lesson 6-1)

Multiplying Inequalities by −1

Work with a partner. Be sure that each of you understands each step in the examples.

Example 1: Solve the inequality.

$$3 - x < -2x$$
$$3 - x + 2x < -2x + 2x \quad \textit{Add 2x to each side.}$$
$$3 + x < 0$$
$$3 + x - 3 < 0 - 3 \quad \textit{Subtract 3 from each side.}$$
$$x < -3$$

Example 2: Suppose that the inequality symbol is an equality symbol in Example 1. The equation might be solved as follows.

$$3 - x = -2x$$
$$3 - x + x = -2x + x \quad \textit{Add x to each side.}$$
$$3 = -x$$
$$-3 = x \quad \textit{Multiply each side by −1.}$$

Example 3: Try to solve the inequality as the equation was solved.

$$3 - x < -2x$$
$$3 - x + x < -2x + x \quad \textit{Add x to each side.}$$
$$3 < -x$$

Another way to state the inequality $3 < -x$ is $-x > 3$. Recall that the solution in Example 1 is $x < -3$. The inequalities $-x > 3$ and $x < -3$ are equivalent. Notice that the directions of the inequality symbols are reversed. In the last step of Example 2, each side of the equation is multiplied by -1. Finish the solution of the inequality.

$$3 < -x$$
$$-3 > x \quad \textit{Multiply each side by −1.}$$

Multiply each side of the following inequalities by −1.

1. $-x > 2$ 2. $-x < 5$ 3. $x < 6$ 4. $x > -7$

5. $-x < -4$ 6. $-x > -8$ 7. $x < -10$ 8. $-x > 0$

9. Complete the following.
   If $a < b$, then $(-1)(a)$_____$(-1)(b)$.
   If $a > b$, then $(-1)(a)$_____$(-1)(b)$.

10. What do you suppose is the result of multiplying each side of an inequality by any negative number?

Algebra Activity Recording Sheet

(Use with the Lesson 6-2 Preview Activity on page 324 in the Student Edition.)

Solving Inequalities

Materials: algebra tiles

Explore
Use algebra tiles to solve each inequality.

1. $-4x < 12$

2. $-2x > 8$

3. $-3x \geq -6$

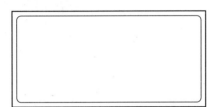

4. $-5x \leq -5$

Make a Conjecture

5. In Exercises 1–4, is the coefficient of x in each inequality positive or negative?

6. Compare the inequality symbols and locations of the variable in Exercises 1–4 with those in their solutions. What do you find?

7. Model the solution for $2x \geq 6$. What do you find? How is this different from solving $-2x \geq 6$?

Algebra Activity

(Use with Algebra 1, Lesson 6-4)

Compound Inequalities

Materials: for each pair of students: scissors, yellow and blue permanent highlighting pens, a copy of this Algebra Activity sheet, a transparency on compound inequalities, and a worksheet for graphing compound inequalities

Preparation: Cut the transparencies and color as indicated below.

Blue A ——————▶   Yellow A ——————▶

Blue B ——————▶   Yellow B ——————▶

1. Write $x \leq 3$ on line 1 and $x > -2$ on line 2 of the transparency.

2. Using the Yellow A model graph on number line 1, graph $x \leq 3$.

3. Using the Blue B model graph on number line 2, graph $x > -2$.

Note: A transparency may be flipped for $x < \_\_$ or $x \leq \_\_\_$.

4. Slide the yellow and blue models to line 3, overlapping the models. Be sure to align the origins from each graph.

5. Identify the solution set for $x \leq 3$ and $x > -2$.

6. Identify the solution set of $x \leq 3$ or $x > -2$.

7. Compare the solution set of $x \leq 3$ and $x > -2$ with the solution set of $x \leq 3$ or $x > -2$.

Note: When graphing "and" compound inequalities, the solution set is green. Solutions to "or" compound inequalities are yellow, blue, or green.

8. Use the models to solve the inequalities on the worksheet containing four compound inequalities.

9. Describe each solution set in your own words.

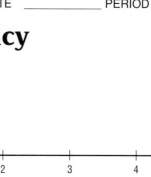

Algebra Activity Transparency
(Use with Algebra 1, Lesson 6-4)

Compound Inequalities (Continued)

1.

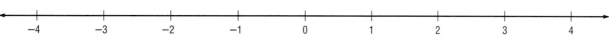

2.

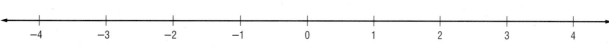

3.

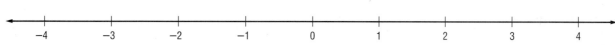

Yellow A

Yellow B

Blue A

Blue B

117

Algebra 1—Chapter 6

1. Graph $x > -3$ and $x < 2$.

$x > -3$

$x < 2$

$-3 < x < 2$

Describe the solution set in your own words. _____

_____

2. Graph $5 > x > 0$.

$5 > x$

$x > 0$

$5 > x > 0$

Describe the solution set in your own words. _____

_____

3. Graph $x > -2$ or $x < 3$.

$x > -2$

$x < 3$

$x > -2$ or $x < 3$

Describe the solution set in your own words. _____

_____

4. Graph $x > -3$ or $x > 1$.

$x > -3$

$x > 1$

$x > -3$ or $x > 1$

Describe the solution set in your own words. _____

_____

Algebra Activity Recording Sheet

(Use with the activity on page 347 in Lesson 6-5 of the Student Edition.)

Absolute Value

Materials: timer or clock with a second hand

Analyze the Data

1. Determine the error by subtracting 60 seconds from each student's time.

2. What does a negative error represent? a positive error?

3. The absolute error is the absolute value of the error. Since absolute value cannot be negative, the absolute error is positive. If the absolute error is 6 seconds, write two possibilities for a student's estimated time of one minute.

4. What estimates would have an absolute error less than 6 seconds?

5. Graph the responses and highlight all values such that $|60 - x| < 6$. How many guesses were within 6 seconds?

119   *Teaching Algebra with Manipulatives*

Using Overhead Manipulatives

(Use with Algebra 1, Lesson 6-6)

Graphing Inequalities

> **Objective** Graph a linear inequality and describe the graph of the inequality.
>
> **Materials**
> - blank transparencies,
> - prepared as described below
> - coordinate grid transparency*
> - transparency pens*   * = available in Overhead Manipulative Resources

Demonstration 1
Graphing $y > 2$, $y < x + 2$

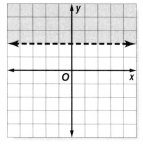

- Prepare transparencies of the graphs of $y > 2$ and $y < x + 2$. For each graph, place a blank transparency over the coordinate grid transparency. Draw each graph.
- Show students the graph. Ask them what the equation of the line is. **$y = 2$**
- Explain that the graph includes all points in the shaded region, but does not include the line. Remind students that when you graph on graph paper, you indicate the non-inclusion of the line by drawing a dashed line. Have the students describe the shaded region. **all points where y is greater than 2, or $y > 2$**
- Ask students how the shaded region relates to the line. **It is above the line.** Ask what region would be shaded to show $y < 2$. **The region below the line.**

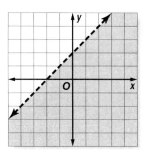

- Show students the graph of $y < x + 2$. Let them know that the line represents $y = x + 2$ and would be dashed on graph paper.
- Point out that the graph is a shaded region. Ask students what points are included in the graph? **all points in the region below the line**
- Ask students to notice that in the first graph, where y was *greater than* an expression, the shaded region was above the line; in the second graph, where y was *less than* expression, the shaded region was below the line. Have students explain why this occurs. **The line represents y equal to the value. Greater values of y are above the line and lesser values are below it.**

Demonstration 2
Graphing $y \geq 3x - 5$ and Other Inequalities

- Prepare a transparency for the graph of $y \geq 3x - 5$. Before displaying the graph, inform students you are going to graph $y \geq 3x - 5$. Ask whether the shaded region will be above or below the graph of the line and why. **Above; y is greater than a value.** Display the graph.

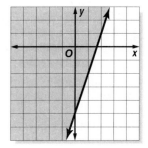

- Point out that in this case y is greater than or equal to $3x - 5$. Ask what points are included in the graph. **all points in the region above the line and on the line**

- Write the following inequalities on a blank transparency. Have students tell what points would be included in the graph of each inequality.

Inequality	Points Included in the Graph of the Inequality
$y < -5$	**all points below the line $y = -5$**
$y \leq 2x + 1$	**all points below the line $y = 2x + 1$ and on the line**
$y > \frac{1}{2}x$	**all points above the line $y = \frac{1}{2}x$**

- On a blank transparency, write the information shown below. Ask students to write the inequality.

Inequality	Points Included in the Graph of the Inequality
$y > 4$	all points above the line $y = 4$
$y \geq 3x - 1$	all points above the line $y = 3x - 1$ and on the line
$y = -4x$	all points on the line $y = -4x$

Solving Systems of Linear Equations and Inequalities
Teaching Notes and Overview

 Mini-Project
Comparing Options
(p. 124 of this booklet)

Use With Lesson 7-1.

Objective Use given information to compare options.

This Mini-Project requires students to work in groups of two. They read information about how their performance on five 100-point tests and the number of times they do their homework in a quarter will affect their grade. The information provides two options in equation form. In the exercises, the groups are asked to graph the equations and choose which option will give the higher grade for the quarter.

Answers

1. See students' graphs; second option

2. See students' graphs; 1st option,
   $y = -\dfrac{1}{100}x + \dfrac{4}{5}$, 2nd option, $y = -\dfrac{1}{150}x + \dfrac{5}{6}$;
   second option

 Algebra Activity Recording Sheet
Using Substitution
(p. 125 of this booklet)

Use With the activity on page 376 in Lesson 7-2 of the Student Edition.

Objective Using substitution to solve systems of equations.

Be sure students are comfortable using the equation mats and the algebra tiles. You may want to review and model a similar system of equations on the mat.

Form groups of two or three to do this activity. Allow sufficient time for students to complete the exercises under the Model and Analyze section. Then go over their responses. Tell each group that you would like to check their equation mat for Exercise 5. Then they may

begin to write their explanation for solving the system using algebra tiles.

Answers
See Teacher Wraparound Edition p. 376.

 Using Overhead Manipulatives
Elimination Using Addition and Subtraction
(p. 126 of this booklet)

Use With Lesson 7-3.

Objective Solve systems of equations by the elimination method using addition and subtraction. The demonstration contains one activity and an extension.

- This demonstration shows students how to use the method of elimination to solve systems of equations. Model $2x - y = 4$ on the equation mat. Review what the tiles represent. Then model $x + y = -10$ on the same mat. Tell that the goal is to get the 1 positive x-tile or the 1 positive y-tile by themselves on one side. Review the process of making zero pairs and arranging tiles on the right side into 3 equal groups so they correspond to the 3 x-tiles. Explain the solution and how to check it.

- The Extension deals with solving a system of equations containing three variables with algebra tiles on the equation mat. Students should be confident about solving a system of equations containing two variables before attempting to work the more complex system. Ask students to check their solution.

Materials
algebra tiles*
equation mat transparency*
* = available in Overhead Manipulative Resources

Answers
Answers appear on the teacher demonstration instructions on page 126.

Algebra Activity

Graphing Systems of Inequalities
(pp. 127–128 of this booklet)

Use With Lesson 7-5.

Objective Graph systems of inequalities.

Materials
classroom set of Algebra Activity worksheets
transparency master of Algebra Activity
blue and yellow acetate

Cut the transparency on the dashed lines.
Cut one blue and one yellow 3″ by 5″ acetate
rectangle.

Review graphing linear equations and
inequalities. Remind students that solid lines
are used for inequalities involving $\geq$ or $\leq$, and
dashed lines are used for inequalities
involving $>$ or $<$.

Graph the inequality $y < x + 2$. Place the blue
acetate rectangle on the graph to illustrate the
area to be shaded. Next, graph $y \geq 3x$ and
shade with the yellow acetate rectangle. Tell
students that the solution to the system is the
green area.

In groups, have students complete the Algebra
Activity worksheet.

Answers

1–6. See students' graphs.

Mini-Project

(Use with Algebra 1, Lesson 7-1)

Comparing Options

Work in pairs. Suppose there will be five 100-point tests each quarter in algebra class. Homework will be checked 25 times each quarter. You figure that you can average 70 points on each of the 5 tests for a total of 70(5), or 350, points.

You are given two options for calculating your grade. The first option is to have 5 points taken off the total of your test scores each time you fail to do a homework assignment.

The second option is to have 4 points added to your total each time you do an assignment. The second option results in the homework acting as a sixth test worth 4(25), or 100, points.

The ratio $y = \dfrac{\text{your points}}{\text{total possible points}}$ determines your grade. The greater the ratio, the better your grade. The highest possible grade is 1.00. Let $x =$ the number of times each quarter that you figure you will not do your homework assignment.

First option

$$y = \frac{350 - 5x}{500}$$

$$y = -\frac{5}{500}x + \frac{350}{500}$$

$$y = -\frac{1}{100}x + \frac{7}{10}$$

Second option

$$y = \frac{350 + 4(25 - x)}{600}$$

$$y = \frac{350 + 100 - 4x}{600}$$

$$y = -\frac{4}{600}x + \frac{450}{600}$$

$$y = -\frac{1}{150}x + \frac{3}{4}$$

1. Use the grid at the right to graph both equations. Which option will give you a higher grade? Remember, the greater the value of y, the higher the grade.

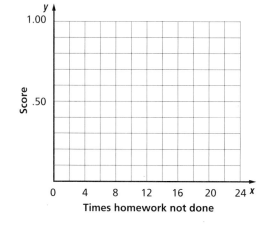

2. Suppose you figure that you can average 80 rather than 70 on the 5 tests. Use the example above to help derive an equation for each option. Graph both equations on the second grid. Which option will give you a higher grade?

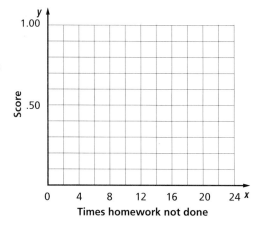

Teaching Algebra with Manipulatives

Algebra Activity Recording Sheet

(Use with the activity on page 376 in Lesson 7-2 of the Student Edition.)

Using Substitution

Materials: algebra tiles, equation mat

Model and Analyze
Since $y = x - 4$, use 1 positive x tile and 4 negative 1 tiles to represent y.
Use algebra tiles to represent $3x + y = 8$.

1. Use what you know about equation mats to solve for x. What is the value of x?

2. Use $y = x - 4$ to solve for y.

3. What is the solution of the system of equations?

Make a Conjecture
4. Explain how to solve the following system of equations using algebra tiles.

$$4x + 3y = 10$$
$$y = x + 1$$

5. Why do you think this method is called substitution?

Teaching Algebra with Manipulatives

Using Overhead Manipulatives

(Use with Algebra 1, Lesson 7-3)

Elimination Using Addition and Subtraction

Objective Solve systems of equations by the elimination method using addition and subtraction.

Materials
- algebra tiles*
- equation mat transparency*

* = available in Overhead Manipulative Resources

Demonstration
Elimination Using Addition and Subtraction

- Place 2 positive *x*-tiles and 1 negative *y*-tile on the left side of the equation mat transparency and 4 positive 1-tiles on the right side. Ask students what equation is represented on the mat. **2*x* − *y* = 4**

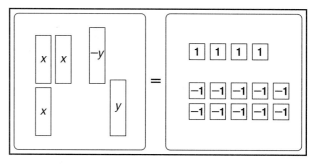

- Below the representation for $2x - y = 4$ on the mat, place 1 positive *x*-tile and 1 positive *y*-tile on the left side of the equation mat and 10 negative 1-tiles on the right side. Have students state what equation is represented below $2x - y = 4$. **x + y = − 10**

- Remind students that, in solving equations, the goal is to get the 1 positive *x*-tile or 1 positive *y*-tile by themselves on one side.

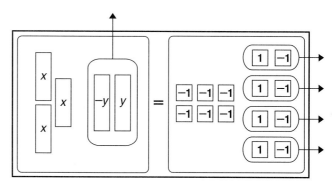

- Review the use of zero pairs in adding and subtracting integers. Tell students that a zero pair of *y*-tiles are formed when a positive *y*-tile is paired with a negative *y*-tile. On the right side of the mat there are 5 zero pairs. Remove all zero pairs.

- Arrange the remaining tiles on the right side into 3 equal groups so they correspond to the 3 *x*-tiles. Ask students how many tiles correspond to each *x*-tile. **2 negative 1-tiles**

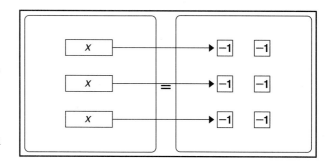

- Have students substitute −2 for *x* in $2x - y = 4$ and in $x + y = -10$ and solve for *y*. Ask students, "What is the solution to the system of equations $2x - y = 4$ and $x + y = -10$?" **−2, −8**

Algebra Activity Transparency Master

(Use with Algebra 1, Lesson 7-5)

Graphing Systems of Inequalities

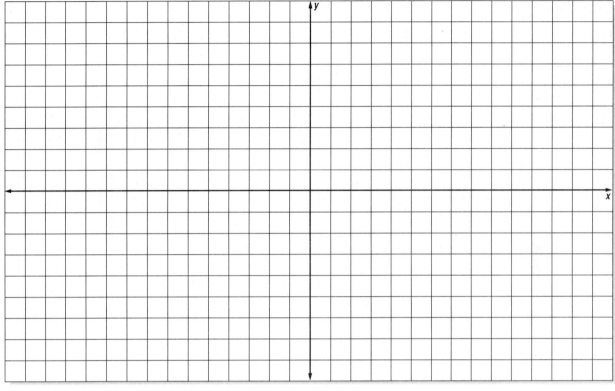

127

Teaching Algebra with Manipulatives

Algebra 1—Chapter 7

Algebra Activity

(Use with Algebra 1, Lesson 7-5)

Graphing Systems of Inequalities

Graph each inequality.

1. $x > 2$

2. $y < x - 1$

3. $2x + y \geq 6$

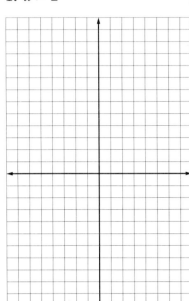 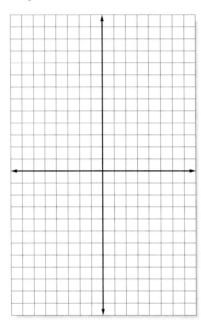 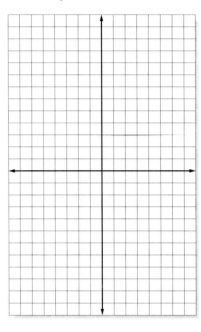

Solve each system of inequalities by graphing.

4. $y > 4$
    $x \leq -1$

5. $y \geq x + 4$
    $y < 2x - 2$

6. $x - y > 1$
    $y - x > 1$

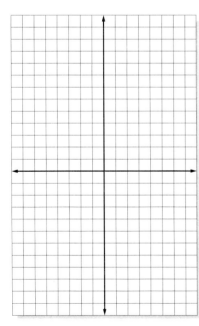 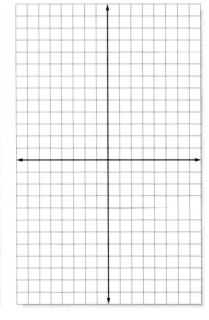 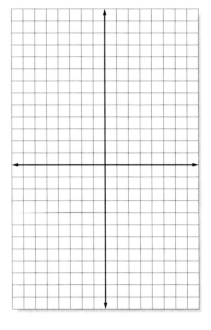

Polynomials
Teaching Notes and Overview

Using Overhead Manipulatives

Multiplying Monomials
(p. 134 of this booklet)

Use With Lesson 8-1.

Objective Multiply monomials using models.

Materials
algebra tiles*
product mat transparency*
transparency pen*
blank transparencies
* = available in Overhead Manipulative Resources

The demonstration is an activity that uses algebra tiles and the area of a rectangle to model multiplying monomials. Students need to know what the 1-tile, x-tile, and x^2-tile represent. $(2x)(x)$ is modeled on the product mat transparency by marking off a length of 2 x-tiles and a width of 1 x-tile. Using the marks as guides, a large rectangle is drawn and covered with x^2-tiles. Students are asked to state the area of the large rectangle, namely, $2x^2$. Provide additional examples showing how to use models to multiply monomials. Discuss with students how you can multiply without using models.

Answers
Answers appear on the teacher demonstration instructions on page 134.

Algebra Activity Recording Sheet

Investigating Surface Area and Volume
(p. 135 of this booklet)

Use With Lesson 8-1 as a follow-up activity. This corresponds to the activity on page 416 in the Student Edition.

Objective Find the surface area and volume of prisms.

Materials
scissors
tape
grid paper

Carefully review the directions to Collect Data at the top of the sheet. Have students work in groups of two or three to complete the Collect the Data section. You will need to supply each group with the materials listed to construct four prisms. Discuss the formulas for finding the surface area and volume of a prism. Once the students have finished making the models, be sure they understand the expectations for the Analyze the Data section. You may want to do part of Exercise 1 as a large group. Go over the surface area and volume of the prism with 2-by-5-by-3 dimensions. Then discuss Prism A, that is, finding the surface area, volume, surface area ratio, and volume ratio. In groups, have them complete Exercises 1 through 5. When the students are ready, discuss the answers to these exercises.

Extending the Investigation is similar to the activity with the prism. However, it deals with the surface area and volume of a cylinder. Review the formulas and the procedure for Collect the Data, Analyze the Data, and Make a Conjecture. Allow time for each group to report on their results.

Answers
See Teacher Wraparound Edition p. 416.

Algebra Activity Recording Sheet

Polynomials
(p. 136 of this booklet)

Use With Lesson 8-4 as a preview activity. This corresponds to the activity on page 431 in the Student Edition.

Objective Model polynomials using algebra tiles.

Materials
algebra tiles*
* = available in Overhead Manipulative Resources

This activity deals with using algebra tiles to model polynomials. Point out that a polynomial is a monomial or the sum of monomials. Make sure students understand what the 1-tile(yellow), x-tile(green) and the x^2-tile(blue) represent and that their opposites are red tiles. Go over the three examples with the class. In groups, have students complete the exercises. As soon as the groups have completed the work, talk about the answers. If some students are having difficulty representing the polynomials with algebra tiles, let them model additional polynomials.

Answers
See Teacher Wraparound Edition p. 431.

Algebra Activity Recording Sheet

Adding and Subtracting Polynomials
(p. 137 of this booklet)

Use With Lesson 8-5 as a preview activity. This corresponds to the activity on pages 437–438 in the Student Edition.

Objective Add and subtract polynomials using models.

Materials
algebra tiles*
* = available in Overhead Manipulative Resources

This activity may be used as a preview to Lesson 8-5. It shows how algebra tiles can be used to model addition and subtraction of polynomials. Students need to know the meaning of like terms, combining like terms, and removing and adding zero pairs. Like terms are represented by tiles that are the same shape and size. Be sure students know that you can remove or add zero pairs without changing the polynomial. Go over Activities 1–3 as a class. Activities 2 and 3 illustrate two ways to model the same subtraction. Point out to students that you can subtract a polynomial by adding its opposite. In groups, have students use algebra tiles to complete the exercises.

Answers
See Teacher Wraparound Edition pp. 437–438.

Using Overhead Manipulatives

Adding and Subtracting Polynomials
(pp. 138–140 of this booklet)

Use With Lesson 8-5.

Objective Add and subtract polynomials using models.

Materials
polynomial models transparency*
algebra tiles*
transparency pen*
blank transparencies
colored acetate sheets (optional)
* = available in Overhead Manipulative Resources

This demonstration contains two activities and an extension.

- Demonstration 1 shows how to add two polynomials using algebra tiles. First, the polynomials to be added are modeled. Then like terms are combined and all zero pairs are removed. The polynomial that remains models the sum.

- Demonstration 2 illustrates subtracting polynomials using algebra tiles. Remind students that subtraction is taking away or removing. The polynomial that remains models the difference.

- The extension deals with adding polynomials that have x^2, xy, and y^2 terms. The y^2-tile is represented by a square that is larger than the x^2-tile. The xy-tile is shown with a length of x and a width of y. You may want to prepare some y^2 and xy models using colored acetate and use these as tiles. Both addends are modeled. Then to find the sum, combine like terms and remove any zero pairs, the remaining tiles represent the sum.

Discuss with students how you can add or subtract polynomials without using models.

Answers
Answers appear on the teacher demonstration instructions on pages 138–140.

Mini-Project

Multiplying Binomials
(p. 141 of this booklet)

Use With Lesson 8-5.

Objective Model and find the product of two binomials.

Materials
algebra tiles*
* = available in Overhead Manipulative Resources

This Mini-Project has students draw a rectangle where the width is one binomial and the length is the other binomial. Write the area of each rectangle inside it. Then add the areas of the individual rectangles, combining those that are like terms. In groups, ask students to read, study and discuss the illustrated example. After the groups have had time to do the latter, call on them to explain each step. Ask them questions to check for understanding. Point out that the binomials $x + 1$ and $3x - 2$ are the length and width of the rectangle. Then add the areas of the individual rectangles and combine those that are like terms. Be sure students know that a tile (-1)-by-(-1) or $(-1)(-1)$ represents 1. Have students use this same procedure to complete the exercises

Answers

1. $x^2 - x - 6$ 2. $2x^2 - x - 1$

3. $4x^2 + 4x - 3$ 4. $x^2 - 9$

5. $x^2 + 8x + 16$ 6. $x^2 - 4x + 4$

Using Overhead Manipulatives

Multiplying a Polynomial by a Monomial
(pp. 142–143 of this booklet)

Use With Lesson 8-6.

Objective Model the product of a binomial and a monomial.

Materials
product mat transparency*
algebra tiles*
transparency pen*
two blank transparencies
* = available in Overhead Manipulative Resources

This demonstration has two activities and an extension.

- Demonstration 1 deals with multiplying a polynomial by a monomial, that is, $x(x + 1)$. Algebra tiles are used in conjunction with the area of a rectangle to model the process. Students should recognize the product as the Distributive Property, namely, $x(x + 1) = (x)(x) + (x)(1)$.

- Demonstration 2 deals again with multiplying a polynomial by a monomial, that is, $2x(x - 3)$. Algebra tiles are used in conjunction with the area of a rectangle to model the process. Review the sign of the product of two integers: $(+)(+) = (+), (-)(-) = (+), (+)(-) = (-), (-)(+) = (-)$. This is another illustration of the Distributive Property.

- The Extension challenges students to use algebra tiles to show a given area, and then find the length and width.

Answers
Answers appear on the teacher demonstration instructions on pages 142–143.

Algebra Activity Recording Sheet

Multiplying Polynomials
(p. 144 of this booklet)

Use With Lesson 8-7 as a preview activity. This corresponds to the activity on pages 450–451 in the Student Edition.

Objective Model and find the product of two binomials.

Materials
algebra tiles*
product mat transparency*
* = available in Overhead Manipulative Resources

As a preview to Lesson 8-7, have students form groups of two or three to complete this recording sheet using algebra tiles. There are three activities used as examples. Discuss each activity, and then have the students use the algebra tiles to model it along with you. The three activities are to use tiles to find: $(x + 2)(x + 5)$; $(x - 1)(x - 4)$; and $(x - 3)(2x + 1)$.

In their groups, have students complete Exercises 1–3. Then go over their answers. Let them do Exercises 4–11 on their own. As soon as the groups are finished, discuss the answers.

Answers
See Teacher Wraparound Edition pp. 450–451.

Using Overhead Manipulatives

Multiplying Polynomials
(pp. 145–146 of this booklet)

Use With Lesson 8-7.

Objective Model and find the product of two binomials.

Materials
algebra tiles*
product mat transparency*
transparency pen*
blank transparency
* = available in Overhead Manipulative Resources

This demonstration contains two activities and an extension.

- Demonstration 1 involves finding the product of two binomials, namely, $(x + 1)(x + 4)$ using algebra tiles.

- Demonstration 2 involves finding the product of two binomials, namely, $(x - 2)(2x + 3)$ using algebra tiles.

- The Extension deals with comparing the use of algebra tiles to find a product with the FOIL method.

Answers
Answers appear on the teacher demonstration instructions on pages 145–146.

Algebra Activity

Multiplying Polynomials
(pp. 147–148 of this booklet)

Use With Lesson 8-7.

Objective Multiply polynomials by using the Distributive Property.

Materials
classroom set of Algebra Activity worksheets
transparency master of Algebra Activity

Before class, cut the figures on the transparency that are below the dashed line and color them if you wish. You may want to make similar sets of squares and rectangles for students from heavy paper.

Discuss how to find the area of figures A–D on the transparency. Students need to know that the area of a rectangle is the product of its length and width.

A Area = $(6)(6)$
B Area = $(6)(4) + (6)(2)$
C Area = $(6)(6) + (6)(-2)$
D Area = $(3)(4) + (3)(2) + (3)(4) + (3)(2)$

Be sure students understand that this is an application of the Distributive Property.

Have students complete Exercises 1–3 on the worksheet.

Assign area values to the models: x-by-$x = x^2$, 1-by-$x = x$ and 1-by-1 = 1. Place the models over matching spaces of figures E–H on the transparency. Discuss finding the products by adding the areas.

E Area = $x(x + 1) = x^2 + x$
F Area = $x(x + 3) = x^2 + 3x$
G Area = $x(x - 2) = x^2 - 2x$
H Area = $(x + 1)(x + 4) = x^2 + 5x + 4$

In groups, have students use diagrams or models to complete the worksheet.

As an extension, challenge students to factor polynomials by creating a rectangle and working backwards.

Answers

1. $(6)(1) + (6)(5) = 36$

2. $(6)(6) + (6)(-2) = 24$

3. $(4)(1) + (4)(5) + (2)(1) + (2)(5) = 36$

4. $x^2 - 2x$ **5.** $x^2 + 3x$

6. $x^2 + 3x + 2$ **7.** $x^2 + x - 12$

8. $3x + 3$ **9.** $2x - 16$

10. $x^2 + 3x$ **11.** $x^2 - 4x$

12. $3x^2 + 2x$ **13.** $x^2 + 10x + 16$

Using Overhead Manipulatives

Three Special Products
(pp. 149–151 of this booklet)

Use With Lesson 8-8.

Objective Model the square of a sum, the square of a difference and the product of a sum and a difference.

Materials
algebra tiles*
product mat transparency*
transparency pen*
blank transparencies
* = available in Overhead Manipulative Resources

This demonstration contains three activities and an extension.

- Demonstration 1 deals with finding the square of a sum, namely, $(x + 1)^2$. Remind students that $(x + 1)^2 = (x + 1)(x + 1)$. So the model is a square that measures $x + 1$ on each side. There are three similar squares along with $(x + 1)^2$ to be examined: $(x + 2)^2 = x^2 + 4x + 4$, $(x + 3)^2 = x^2 + 6x + 9$ and $(x + 4)^2 = x^2 + 8x + 16$.

  Students are asked to determine if there is a relationship between the terms of the binomial and the terms of the equivalent trinomial. Also, using this relationship, students are asked to find $(x + 8)^2$ without modeling and to check their result using the FOIL method.

- Demonstration 2 focuses on finding the square of a difference, namely, $(x - 1)^2$. Once again students need to know that $(-1)(-1) = 1$. This activity mirrors Demonstration 1, except it deals with the square of a difference. Students are asked to determine a relationship between the terms of the binomial and the terms of the equivalent trinomial. Using this relationship they are asked to find $(x - 8)^2$ without modeling and to check their result using the FOIL method.

- Demonstration 3 is about finding the product of a sum and a difference. After examining three similar types of these multiplications, students are asked to derive a general form for finding the product, namely, $(a + b)(a - b) = a^2 - b^2$.

- The Extension involves modeling and finding more products.

Answers
Answers appear on the teacher demonstration instructions on pages 149–151.

Algebra 1—Chapter 8

Using Overhead Manipulatives

(Use with Algebra 1, Lesson 8-1)

Multiplying Monomials

Objective Multiply monomials using models.

Materials
- algebra tiles*
- product mat transparency*
- transparency pen*
- blank transparencies

* = available in Overhead Manipulative Resources

Demonstration
Multiplying Monomials

- Remind students that the area of a rectangle can be used to model multiplication, and that the width and length represent factors. Draw a rectangle on a blank transparency and label the width 8 and the length 4. Ask students to state the area of this rectangle. **(8)(4) or 32 square units**

- Remove the transparency (it will be used later). Display a 1-unit tile. Tell students that the length of each side is 1 unit. Ask them what the area of the tile is. **(1)(1) or 1 square unit** Write a 1 in the center of the tile.

- Display an x-tile. Point out that the width is the same as the width of the 1-tile, 1 unit. Tell them that the length is x units. Ask them what the area of the tile is. **1x or x square units** Write an x in the center of the tile.

- Display an x^2-tile. Point out that the length and width are both x units. Ask students what the area of the tile is. **x^2 square units** Write x^2 in the center of the tile.

- Tell students you want to find $(2x)(x)$. Display the product mat transparency. Remind students that the length of an x-tile is x units. Ask how you could model the length $2x$. **the length of 2 x-tiles** Use an x-tile to mark off a length of $2x$ units.

- Use an x-tile to mark off a width of x units. Using the marks as guides, draw a large rectangle and cover it with area tiles.

- Ask students what the area of the rectangle is. **$2x^2$** Write $(2x)(x) = 2x^2$ below the model.

- Ask students to model $(4)(2x)$. **See students' models.**

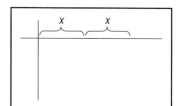

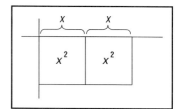

Algebra Activity Recording Sheet

(Use with the Lesson 8-1 Follow-Up Activity on page 416 in the Student Edition.)

Investigating Surface Area and Volume

Materials: scissors, tape, grid paper

Analyze the Data

1. Complete the table using the prisms you made.

Prism	Dimensions	Surface Area (cm^2)	Volume (cm^3)	Surface Area Ratio $\left(\dfrac{SA \text{ of New}}{SA \text{ of Original}}\right)$	Volume Ratio $\left(\dfrac{V \text{ of New}}{V \text{ of Original}}\right)$
Original	2 by 5 by 3	62	30		
A	4 by 10 by 6				
B	6 by 15 by 9				

2. Make a prism with different dimensions from any in this activity. Repeat the steps in **Collect the Data**, and make a table similar to the one in Exercise 1.

Make a Conjecture

3. Suppose you multiply each dimension of a prism by 2. What is the ratio of the surface area of the new prism to the surface area of the original prism? _____

What is the ratio of the volumes? _____

4. Suppose you multiply each dimension of a prism by 3. What is the ratio of the surface area of the new prism to the surface area of the original prism? _____

What is the ratio of the volumes? _____

5. Suppose you multiply each dimension of a prism by a. Make a conjecture about the ratios of surface areas and volumes.

Extend the Activity

6. Do the conjectures you made in Exercise 5 hold true for cylinders? Explain.

Algebra 1—Chapter 8

NAME _____ DATE _____ PERIOD ____

Algebra Activity Recording Sheet

(Use with the Lesson 8-4 Preview Activity on page 431 in the Student Edition.)

Polynomials

Materials: algebra tiles

Model and Analyze

Use algebra tiles to model each polynomial. Then draw a diagram of your model.

1. $-2x^2$

2. $5x - 4$

3. $3x^2 - x$

4. $x^2 + 4x + 3$

Write an algebraic expression for each model.

5.

6.

7.

8.

 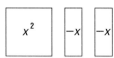

9. Make a Conjecture Write a sentence or two explaining why algebra tiles are sometimes called *area tiles*.

Algebra Activity Recording Sheet

(Use with the Lesson 8-5 Preview Activity on pages 437–438 in the Student Edition.)

Adding and Subtracting Polynomials

Materials: algebra tiles

Model and Analyze
Use algebra tiles to find each sum or difference.

1. $(5x^2 + 3x - 4) + (2x^2 - 4x + 1)$

2. $(2x^2 + 5) + (3x^2 - 2x + 6)$

3. $(-4x^2 + x) + (5x - 2)$

4. $(3x^2 + 4x + 2) - (x^2 - 5x - 5)$

5. $(-x^2 + 7x) - (2x^2 + 3x)$

6. $(8x + 4) - (6x^2 + x - 3)$

7. Find $(2x^2 - 3x + 1) - (2x + 3)$ using each method from Activity 2 and Activity 3. Illustrate with drawings and explain in writing how zero pairs are used in each case.

Using Overhead Manipulatives

(Use with Algebra 1, Lesson 8-5)

Adding and Subtracting Polynomials

Objective Add and subtract polynomials using models.

Materials
- polynomial models transparency*
- overhead algebra tiles*
- transparency pen*
- blank transparencies
- colored acetate sheets (optional)

* = available in Overhead Manipulative Resources

Demonstration 1
Adding Polynomials

- Use the polynomial models transparency to explain guidelines for using algebra tiles.

- Remove the transparency. Place a blank transparency on the screen. Tell students you want to find the sum of $(2x^2 - 3x + 2)$ and $(-4x^2 - x - 4)$. Write the sum on the transparency. Ask students to model the two polynomials.

$2x^2 - 3x + 2$ $-4x^2 - x - 4$

 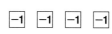

- Inform students that to find the sum, you must combine like terms and remove all zero pairs. Ask them what polynomial model remains.
  $-2x^2 - 4x - 2$ Complete the addition sentence on the transparency.

  $-2x^2 - 4x - 2$

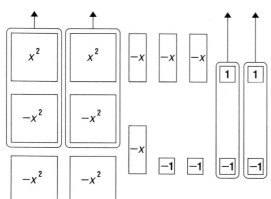

Demonstration 2
Subtracting Polynomials

- Tell students you want to find the difference of $(3x^2 + 4x)$ and $(x^2 + 2x - 2)$. Write $(3x^2 + 4x) - (x^2 + 2x - 2)$ on the blank transparency. Ask students to model $3x^2 + 4x$.

- Remind students that subtraction is taking away or removing. You need to remove 1 positive x^2 tile, 2 positive x tiles, and 2 negative 1 tiles. Ask students how 2 negative 1 tiles can be removed. **Add 2 zero pairs, then remove the 2 negative 1 tiles.** Remove those tiles.

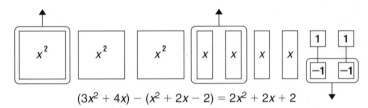

$$(3x^2 + 4x) - (x^2 + 2x - 2) = 2x^2 + 2x + 2$$

- Ask students what tiles remain and what polynomial they represent. **2 positive x^2 tiles, 2 positive x tiles, and 2 positive 1 tiles; $2x^2 + 2x + 2$** Complete the subtraction sentence on the transparency.

Extension
Adding Polynomials Containing x^2, xy and y^2

- Tell students you want to find the sum of $(x^2 + 2xy - y^2)$ and $(2x^2 - xy + y^2)$. Write the addition sentence at the top of the blank transparency.

- Place an x^2 tile on the screen. Then draw a square larger than the x^2 tile. Tell students that this square represents y^2. Mark a negative sign on it to represent $-y^2$. Ask students how they could represent the product xy. (Draw a rectangle x-by-y.) (You can prepare some y^2 and xy models using colored acetate and use these as tiles.)

Model the first addend.

$x^2 + 2xy - y^2$

x^2	xy	$-y^2$
	xy	

Algebra 1—Chapter 8

- Ask students to model the second addend.
$2x^2 - xy + y^2$

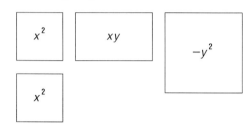

- Combine like terms and remove any zero pairs. Ask students to state the sum. **$3x^2 + xy$**

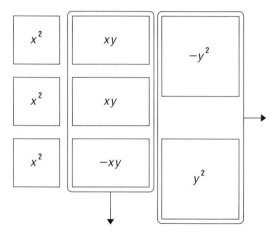

Mini-Project

(Use with Algebra 1, Lesson 8-5)

Multiplying Binomials

Work in small groups. You can find the product of two binomials, $(x + 1)(3x - 2)$, by finding the area of a rectangle.

Step 1   Draw a rectangle whose width represents one binomial and whose length represents the other binomial. Use a longer segment to represent x and a shorter segment to represent 1. $-x$ and -1 can be represented by squiggly lines.

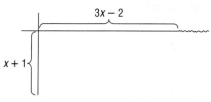

Step 2   Complete the rectangle by drawing the remaining sides of each individual rectangle. Write the area of each rectangle inside it.

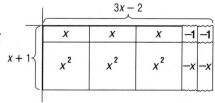

Step 3   Add the areas of the individual rectangles, combining those that are like terms.

$$\text{Area} = 3x^2 + 3x - 2x - 2$$
$$= 3x^2 + x - 2$$

Would the square at the right represent 1 or -1? Justify your answer.

$-1 \;\square$
$\quad\; -1$

Use the procedure shown above to find each product.

1. $(x + 2)(x - 3)$ **2.** $(x - 1)(2x + 1)$

3. $(2x - 1)(2x + 3)$ **4.** $(x + 3)(x - 3)$

5. $(x + 4)(x + 4)$ **6.** $(x - 2)(x - 2)$

Algebra 1—Chapter 8

Using Overhead Manipulatives
(Use with Algebra 1, Lesson 8-6)

Multiplying a Polynomial by a Monomial

> **Objective** Model the product of a binomial and a monomial.
>
> **Materials**
> - product mat transparency*
> - algebra tiles*
> - transparency pen*
> - two blank transparencies
> * = available in Overhead Manipulative Resources

Demonstration 1
Multiplying a Binomial by a Monomial

- Point out that algebra tiles used in previous activities are based on the fact that the area of a rectangle is the product of its width and length. Tell students they will use algebra tiles to build larger rectangles. The length and width of the large rectangle will each represent a polynomial and the area of the large rectangle will each represent their product.
- Tell students you want to find $x(x + 1)$.
- Ask students how to model the length x. **Use the length of an x tile.**
- Display the product mat transparency. Use an x tile to mark off a width of x units.

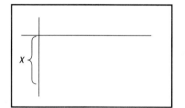

- Ask students how to model $x + 1$. **an x tile and a x tile** Use an x tile and a 1 tile to mark off a length of $x + 1$ units.

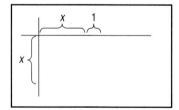

- Using the marks as guides, draw a large rectangle and cover it with algebra tiles.

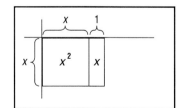

- Ask students what the dimensions of the rectangle are. **x-by-$x + 1$** Ask them to state the area of the rectangle as an algebraic expression. **$x(x + 1)$**
- Ask students to add the values represented by the tiles to find the area of the rectangle modeled. **$x^2 + x$**
- Write $x(x + 1) = x^2 + x$ below the model.

Demonstration 2
Multiplying a Binomial by a Monomial
- Clear the mat. Tell students you want to find $2x(x - 3)$.
- Ask students how to model the length $2x$. **$2x$ tiles**
- Use an x tile to mark off a width of $2x$ units.
- Use an x tile and a 1 tile to mark off a length of $x - 3$ as shown at the right.

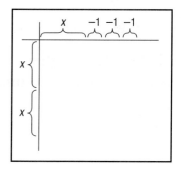

- Using the marks as guides, draw a large rectangle and cover it with 2 yellow x^2 tiles and 6 red x tiles. Point out that yellow tiles represent the areas with positive dimensions and red tiles represent areas with 1 negative and 1 positive dimension. Ask students to explain this use of the tiles. **The product of two positive numbers is positive; the product of a positive and a negative number is negative.**
  Ask what color tile would be used if both dimensions were negative and why. **Yellow; the product of two negative numbers is positive.**

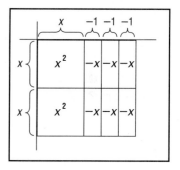

- Ask students what the dimensions of the rectangle are. **$2x$ by $(x - 3)$** Have them state the area of the rectangle as an algebraic expression. **$2x(x - 3)$**
- Ask students to add the values represented by the tiles to find the area of the rectangle modeled. **$2x^2 - 6x$**
- Write $2x(x - 3) = 2x^2 - 6x$ below the model.

Extension
Given the Area, Model and Find the Length and Width
Have students make possible rectangles for each area. Then have them find the length and width.

a. $2x^2 + 4x + 2, 2x$ **b.** $3x + 6x + 2, 3$

Algebra 1—Chapter 8

Algebra Activity Recording Sheet

(Use with the Lesson 8-7 Preview Activity on pages 450–451 in the Student Edition.)

Multiplying Polynomials

Materials: algebra tiles, product mat

Model and Analyze
Use algebra tiles to find each product.

1. $(x + 2)(x + 3)$

2. $(x - 1)(x - 3)$

3. $(x + 1)(x - 2)$

4. $(x + 1)(2x + 1)$

5. $(x - 2)(2x - 3)$

6. $(x + 3)(2x - 4)$

7. You can also use the Distributive Property to find the product of two binomials. The figure at the right shows the model for $(x + 3)(x + 4)$ separated into four parts. Write a sentence or two explaining how this model shows the use of the Distributive Property.

| x^2 | | x | x | x | x |

x		1	1	1	1
x		1	1	1	1
x		1	1	1	1

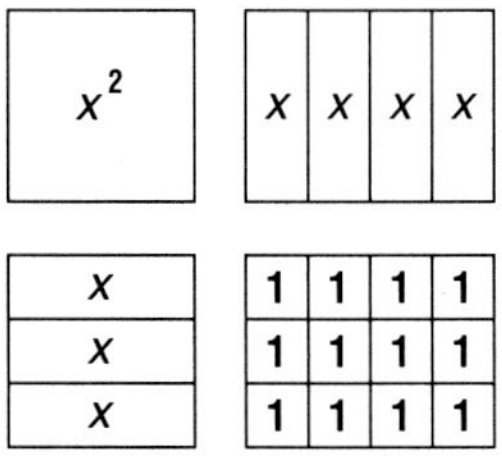

Using Overhead Manipulatives
(Use with Algebra 1, Lesson 8-7)

Multiplying Polynomials

Objective Model products of binomials.

Materials
• product mat transparency*
• algebra tiles*
• transparency pen*
• blank transparency
* = available in Overhead Manipulative Resources

Demonstration 1
Product of Two Binomials
• Tell students you want to find $(x + 1)(x + 4)$.

• Display the product mat transparency. Use algebra tiles to mark a width of $x + 1$ and a length of $x + 4$.

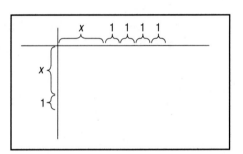

• Using the marks as a guide, draw a large rectangle and cover it with tiles. Ask students what polynomial is modeled. $x^2 + 5x + 4$ Ask what the product of $x + 1$ and $x + 4$ is. $x^2 + 5x + 4$

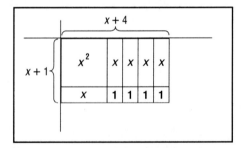

Teacher Demonstration 2
Product of Two Binomials
• Tell students you want to find $(x - 2)(2x + 3)$.

• On the product mat, use tiles to mark a width of $x - 2$ and a length of $2x + 3$.

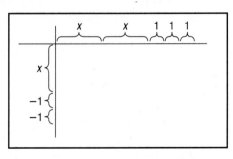

(continued on the next page)

- Using the marks as a guide, draw a large rectangle and cover it with tiles. Begin with 2 yellow x^2 tiles and 3 yellow x tiles to represent x-by-x and x-by-1 areas. Ask students what tiles to use to represent -1-by-x areas. **red x tiles** Place 4 red x tiles on the rectangle. Ask what tiles to use to represent -1-by-1 areas. **red 1 tiles** Position 6 red 1 tiles to complete the rectangle.

- Rearrange the tiles to simplify the polynomial. Ask if there are any zero pairs that can be removed. **Yes, there are 3 x tile zero pairs.** Remove the zero pairs. Ask students what polynomial is modeled. **$2x^2 - x - 6$**

- Ask what the product of $x - 2$ and $2x + 3$ is. **$2x^2 - x - 6$**

Extension
Foil Method to Multiply Two Binomials

- Place the tiles from Demonstration 2 back on the large rectangle. Place a blank transparency on top of the model. Outline the following rectangles: x by $2x$, x by 3, -2 by $2x$, and -2 by 3.

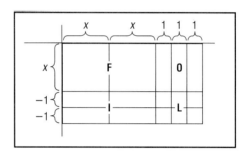

- Ask students to match the rectangles with the steps of the **FOIL** method for multiplying binomials. You may want to review the meaning of the FOIL method.

F = product of **First** terms of binomials $\qquad (x)(2x) = 2x^2$

O = product of **Outer** terms of binomials $\qquad (x)(3) = 3x$

I = product of **Inside** terms of binomials $\qquad (-2)(2x) = -4x$

L = product of **Last** terms of binomials $\qquad (-2)(3) = -6$

- Write $2x^2 - x - 6$ below the rectangle.

Algebra Activity Transparency

(Use with Algebra 1, Lesson 8-7)

Multiplying Polynomials

Find the area of the region bounded by the solid line.

A

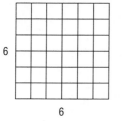

6

6

B

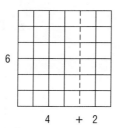

6

4 + 2

C

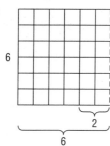

6

6   2

D

3
+
3

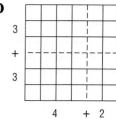

4 + 2

E

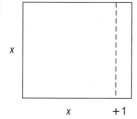

x

x   +1

F

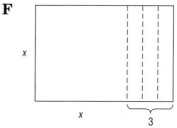

x

x   3

G

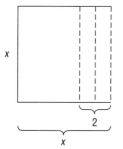

x

2

x

H

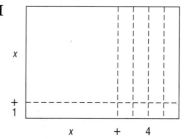

x

+
1

x   +   4

Teaching Algebra with Manipulatives

Algebra 1—Chapter 8

Algebra Activity

(Use with Algebra 1, Lesson 8-7)

Multiplying Polynomials

Draw a diagram and find each product.

Example: $6(3 + 3)$

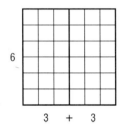

6

3 + 3

$= \underline{\ 6 \cdot 3 + 6 \cdot 3 = 36\ }$

1. $6(1 + 5)$

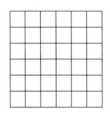

= _____

2. $6(6 - 2)$

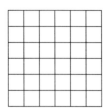

= _____

3. $(4 + 2)(1 + 5)$

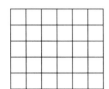

= _____

Example: $x(x - 1)$

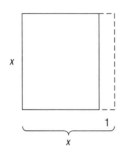

x

1

x

$= \underline{\quad x^2 - x \quad}$

4. $x(x - 2)$

= _____

5. $x(x + 3)$

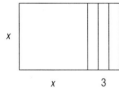

x

x   3

= _____

6. $(x + 1)(x + 2)$

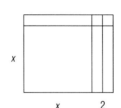

x

x   2

= _____

7. $(x + 4)(x - 3)$

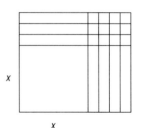

x

x

= _____

Draw a diagram or use models to find each product.

8. $3(x + 1) =$ _____

9. $2(x - 8) =$ _____

10. $x(x + 3) =$ _____

11. $x(x - 4) =$ _____

12. $x(3x + 2) =$ _____

13. $(x + 2)(x + 8) =$ _____

Using Overhead Manipulatives

(Use with Algebra 1, Lesson 8-8)

Three Special Products

Objective Model the square of a sum, the square of a difference, and the product of a sum and a difference

Materials
- product mat transparency*
- algebra tiles*
- transparency pen*
- blank transparencies

* = available in Overhead Manipulative Resources

Demonstration 1
Finding the Square of a Sum

- Tell students you want to find $(x + 1)^2$. Remind them that $(x + 1)^2$ means $(x + 1)(x + 1)$ so you want to model a square that measures $x + 1$ on each side.

- On the product mat transparency, use an x-tile to mark off a square $x + 1$ units on each side.

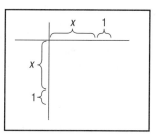

- Using the marks as guides, complete the square by filling it in with tiles.

- Ask students what the area of the large square is. $x^2 + 2x + 1$

- Ask students what $(x + 1)^2$ is. $x^2 + 2x + 1$

- Have students model $(x + 2)^2$.

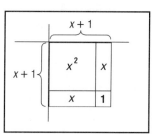

- Ask students what the area of the large square is. $x^2 + 4x + 4$

- Have students model $(x + 3)^2$.

- Ask students what the area of the large square is. $x^2 + 6x + 9$

- Have students model $(x + 4)^2$.

- Ask students what the area of the large square is. $x^2 + 8x + 16$

- On a blank transparency, list four equations that represent the the areas of the four large squares:

$(x + 1)^2 = x^2 + 2x + 1$
$(x + 2)^2 = x^2 + 4x + 4$
$(x + 3)^2 = x^2 + 6x + 9$
$(x + 4)^2 = x^2 + 8x + 16$

- Ask students if there is a relationship between the terms of the binomial and the terms of its equivalent trinomial. **Yes, the first and last terms of the trinomial are squares of the respective terms of the binomial, and the middle term of the trinomial is twice the product of the first and second terms of the binomial.**

- Have students find $(x + 8)^2$ without modeling. $x^2 + 16x + 64$ Then ask them to check their result using the FOIL method.

Demonstration 2
Finding the Product of a Difference

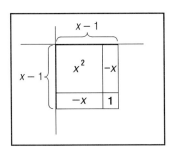

- Tell students you want to find $(x - 1)^2$.
- Place 1 yellow x^2 tile, 2 red x tiles, and 1 yellow 1 tile on a blank transparency to form a square.
- Ask students to state the length of the sides of the square. **$x - 1$**
- Ask students why the 1 tiles are yellow. **The product of -1 and -1 is 1.**
- Ask them to state the area of the large square. **$x^2 - 2x + 1$**

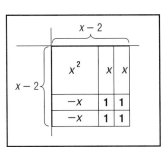

- Clear the screen. Place tiles on the blank transparency to model $(x - 2)^2$.
- Ask students to state the length of the sides of the square. **$x - 2$**
- Ask what the area of the large square is. **$x^2 - 4x + 4$**
- Have students model $(x - 3)^2$ and then $(x - 4)^2$. Ask them to state the area of each large square. **$(x - 3)^2 = x^2 - 6x + 9$, $(x - 4)^2 = x^2 - 8x + 16$**
- On a blank transparency, list the four equations that represent the areas of the four large squares:

$(x - 1)^2 = x^2 - 2x + 1$
$(x - 2)^2 = x^2 - 4x + 4$
$(x - 3)^2 = x^2 - 6x + 9$
$(x - 4)^2 = x^2 - 8x + 16$

- Ask students if there is a relationship between the terms of the binomial and the terms of its equivalent trinomial. **Yes, the first and last terms of the trinomial are squares of the respective terms of the binomial, and the middle term of the trinomial is twice the product of the first and second terms of the binomial.**
- Have students find $(x - 8)^2$ without modeling. **$x^2 - 16x + 64$** Then ask them to check their result using the FOIL method.

Demonstration 3
Finding the Product of a Sum and a Difference

- Place 1 yellow x^2 tile, 1 yellow x tile, 1 red x tile, and 1 red 1 tile on a blank transparency to form a square.

- Ask students, "This is a model of the product of what two binomials?" **($x + 1$) and ($x - 1$)**
  Ask why the 1 tile is red. **The product of 1 and −1 is −1.**

- Review the use of zero pairs in adding and subtracting integers. Tell students that zero pairs of tiles are formed when a positive tile is paired with a negative tile of the same size and shape. Remove all zero pairs.

- Ask students what kind of tiles remain and how many there are of each. **1 positive x^2 tile and 1 negative 1 tile.**

- Ask them to write the simplest form of the product of $x + 1$ and $x - 1$. **$x^2 - 1$.**

- Have students repeat the procedure to model the products of $(x + 2)(x - 2)$, $(x + 3)(x - 3)$, and $(x + 4)(x - 4)$. **$x^2 - 4$; $x^2 - 9$; $x^2 - 16$**

- Tell students to use the patterns found in the above products to derive a general form for the product of $(a + b)(a - b)$. **$(a + b)(a - b) = a^2 - b^2$**

Extension
Modeling and Finding More Products

- Have students make possible rectangles to model and find each product.

  a. $(2x + 2)^2$
  $4x^2 + 8x + 4$

  b. $(2x - 2)^2$
  $4x^2 - 8x - 4$

  c. $(2x - 3)(2x + 3)$
  $4x^2 - 9$

Factoring
Teaching Notes and Overview

Algebra Activity Recording Sheet

Factoring Using the Distributive Property
(p. 156 of this booklet)

Use With Lesson 9-2 as a preview activity. This corresponds to the activity on page 480 in the Student Edition.

Objective Model and factor binomials using the Distributive Property and algebra tiles.

Materials
product mat*
algebra tiles*
* = available in Overhead Manipulative Resources

This activity deals with using algebra tiles and a product mat to model and factor binomials. Guide students through Activities 1 and 2 illustrated on the Algebra Recording Sheet. First, the polynomial is modeled using the tiles. Next, the tiles are arranged into a rectangle. The total area of the rectangle represents the product, and the factors are represented by its length and width. Have students begin the exercises. In Exercise 9, students should discover that if a binomial cannot be represented as a rectangle using the tiles, then it cannot be factored.

Answers
See Teacher Wraparound Edition p. 480.

 ### *Using Overhead Manipulatives*

Factoring Using the Distributive Property
(pp. 157–158 of this booklet)

Use With Lesson 9-2.

Objective Model and factor binomials using the Distributive Property and algebra tiles.

Materials
algebra tiles*
polynomial models transparency*
transparency pen*

blank transparencies
red and yellow acetate, if available
* = available in Overhead Manipulative Resources

This demonstration contains two activities.

- Demonstration 1 uses algebra tiles to model a binomial. Then the tiles are arranged to form a rectangle. The length and width of the rectangle are the factors of the binomial.

- Demonstration 2 involves factoring $2x^2 + 4xy$. Students are asked to model the binomial and form a rectangle. Students find out that $x(2x + 4xy)$ is not completely factored, because each term on $2x + 4xy$ has a common factor, namely, $2x$. Another rectangle needs to be formed. Students find $2x(x + 2y)$.

Answers
Answers appear on the teacher demonstration instructions on pages 157–158.

 ### *Algebra Activity Recording Sheet*

Factoring Trinomials
(p. 159 of this booklet)

Use With Lesson 9-3 as a preview activity. This corresponds to the activity on pages 487–488 in the Student Edition.

Objective Model and factor trinomials using algebra tiles.

Materials
product mat*
algebra tiles*
* = available in Overhead Manipulative Resources

Activities 1 through 4 illustrate how to factor trinomials using algebra tiles. If a trinomial represents the area of a rectangle formed by tiles, then the rectangle's length and width are factors of the area. If a rectangle cannot be formed, then the trinomial is not factorable.

Have students work in small groups to work the exercises. Discuss the answers. Have each group give their examples from Exercise 13. Ask a student to read each group's paragraph.

Answers
See Teacher Wraparound Edition pp. 487–488.

Using Overhead Manipulatives

Factoring Trinomials
(pp. 160–161 of this booklet)

Use With Lesson 9-3.

Objective Model and factor trinomials using algebra tiles.

Materials
algebra tiles*
polynomial models transparency*
transparency pen*
blank transparencies
* = available in Overhead Manipulative Resources

This demonstration contains two activities.

- Demonstration 1 deals with factoring $x^2 + 5x + 6$ using tiles.

- Demonstration 2 involves factoring $x^2 + 3x - 4$. Students are asked to model the trinomial using tiles, and then to form a rectangle with the tiles. In order to form the rectangle, there is a need to add a zero pair of x tiles. Also, students learn that there cannot be a negative 1 tile with a positive width and a positive length.

Answers
Answers appear on the teacher demonstration instructions on pages 160–161.

Using Overhead Manipulatives

Factoring Trinomials
(p. 162 of this booklet)

Use With Lesson 9-4.

Objective Model and factor trinomials using algebra tiles.

Materials
algebra tiles*
polynomial models transparency*
transparency pen*
blank transparencies
* = available in Overhead Manipulative Resources

This demonstration involves an activity for factoring $2x^2 + 3x + 1$ using algebra tiles. First, students are asked to model the trinomial. The importance of being able to fit the x tile(s) after the x^2 tile(s) and 1 tile(s) are placed is emphasized. Students are asked why the latter is similar to making an organized list of factors and their sum as is shown in the Student Edition.

Answers
Answers appear on the teacher demonstration instructions on page 162.

Algebra Activity

Factoring Trinomials
(pp. 163–164 of this booklet)

Use With Lesson 9-4.

Objective Model and factor trinomials using algebra tiles.

Materials
product mat*
algebra tiles*
classroom set of Algebra Activity worksheets
transparency master of Algebra Activity
* = available in Overhead Manipulative Resources

Cut the transparency on the dashed line, then cut the squares and rectangles apart.

Cover Figures 1 and 2 on the Algebra Activity Transparency. Ask students to identify the area of the exposed figures.

Have students make a model of $x^2 + xy$ with the algebra tiles. Uncover Figure 1 on the transparency and discuss the length and width of the rectangle. Have students state the factors.

Ask students to make a model of $x^2 + 2xy + y^2$ with the algebra tiles. Uncover Figure 2 on the transparency and discuss the length and width of the rectangle. Ask students to state the factors of $x^2 + 2xy + y^2$. As a group or individual activity, complete the worksheet. Discuss Exercise 5.

Answers

1. See students' pictures.

2. $x + 2y$; $x + 3y$

3. factors of the product of the area

4. $(2x + y)$ by $(x + y)$; $(x + 2y)$ by $(x + y)$

5. The dimensions of the rectangle represent the two factors of the trinomial, which is the area of the rectangle.

Using Overhead Manipulatives

Factoring Differences of Squares
(pp. 165–166 of this booklet)

Use With Lesson 9-5.

Objective Model and factor differences of squares using algebra tiles.

Materials
algebra tiles*
transparency pens*
straightedge
blank transparencies
colored acetate, if available
* = available in Overhead Manipulative Resources

This demonstration consists of an activity and an extension.

- The demonstration features using one large square and a smaller square to illustrate factoring the differences of squares. The area of the large square is a^2 and the smaller is b^2. Students are asked to place the small square in the upper right corner of the large square and to shade the remaining part of the large square. Then students find the area of the shaded part by cutting it into two trapezoids.

  Next, the two trapezoids are rearranged to form a rectangle. The length is $a + b$ and the width is $a - b$. The area is $a^2 - b^2$.

  Thus, $a^2 - b^2 = (a + b)(a - b)$. Then students are asked to generalize about factoring differences of squares.

- The Extension deals with using algebra tiles to find the differences of squares. Students are lead to see that to make a square with the tiles, a zero pair of xy tiles are needed to complete the square. Once again, students are reminded that adding a zero pair of tiles does not change the value.

Answers
Answers appear on the teacher demonstration instructions on pages 165–166.

Algebra Activity Recording Sheet

Difference of Squares
(p. 167 of this booklet)

Use With the activity on page 501 in Lesson 9-5 of the Student Edition.

Objective Model and illustrate the difference of squares by constructing a rectangle from two congruent parts of a square and finding its area.

Materials
straightedge
scissors

This activity deals with using the area of squares and rectangles to model the difference of squares. Students will draw one square inside and similar to another square. The smaller square is removed, and the remaining portion is cut into two congruent pieces. These pieces then fit together to make a rectangle.

Answers
See Teacher Wraparound Edition p. 501.

Using Overhead Manipulatives

Factoring Perfect Square Trinomials
(pp. 168–169 of this booklet)

Use With Lesson 9-6.

Objective Model and factor perfect square trinomials using algebra tiles.

Materials
algebra tiles*
polynomial models transparency*
transparency pen*
blank transparencies
* = available in Overhead Manipulative Resources

This demonstration deals with two activities and an extension.

- Demonstration 1 involves factoring the perfect square trinomial $x^2 - 2x + 1$. Algebra tiles are used to model the factoring.

- Demonstration 2 deals with factoring the perfect square trinomial $x^2 + 4x + 4$. Algebra tiles are used to model the factoring.

- The Extension focuses on analyzing the information gained from the demonstrations.

Answers
Answers appear on pages 168–169.

Mini-Project
Multiplying Trinomial Squares
(p. 170 of this booklet)
Use With Lesson 9-6.

Objective Model and factor perfect square trinomials using algebra tiles.

Materials
algebra tiles*
* = available in Overhead Manipulative Resources

Have students work in small groups to draw the rectangular regions that model each trinomial.

Algebra tiles may be used for this activity. You may want to check the models made by each group. Discuss the answers when the groups are ready. Allow time to exchange and share ideas on Exercises 9 through 12. Have students show their model for Exercise 12.

Answers

1. They are the same.   2. $(x + 2)$ by $(x + 2)$

3. $(x + 3)^2$ 4. $(2x + 1)^2$

5. $(x + 3)(x + 1)$ 6. $(x + 1)^2$

7. $(x + 4)^2$ 8. $(3x + 1)(x + 1)$

9. $x^2 + 6x + 9, 4x^2 + 4x + 1, x^2 + 2x + 1,$
   $x^2 + 8x + 16$

10. perfect square trinomial

11. The first and third terms are squares and the middle term is twice the product of the square roots of the first and third terms.

12. $(x + 2)(x - 2)$

Algebra Activity
Factoring Trinomial Squares
(pp. 171–172 of this booklet)
Use With Lesson 9-6.

Objective Model and factor trinomial squares using algebra tiles.

Materials
product mat*   algebra tiles*
classroom set of Algebra Activity worksheets
transparency master of Algebra Activity
* = available in Overhead Manipulative Resources

Cut the transparency on the dashed line. Then cut the squares and rectangles apart.

Display the transparency and identify the representation of each shape. Algebra tiles may also be used. Arrange the model of $x^2 + 2x + 1$ to form a square.

Ask students to state the length of each side. Ask what the relationship is between the length of the sides and the factors of $x^2 + 2x + 1$.

Display $x^2 + 4x + 4$ on the transparency and arrange the models to form a square. Have students use algebra tiles at their seats if they wish.

Students may cut their own models or use algebra tiles to complete the worksheet.

Answers

1. They are the same.   2. $(x + 2)$ by $(x + 2)$

3. $(x + 3)^2$ 4. $(2x + 1)^2$

5. $(x + 1)(x + 3)$ 6. $(x + 1)^2$

7. $2(x + 2)^2$ 8. $(x + 4)^2$

9. $(3x + 1)^2$ 10. $(3x + 1)(x + 1)$

11. $(x + 2)(x - 2)$ 12. 1, 3, 4, 6, 7, 8, 9

13. a perfect square trinomial

14. The first term is a perfect square, last term is a perfect square, and the middle term must be twice the product of the square roots of the first and last terms.

15. Write two factors that are the sum or difference of the square root of the first and last terms (and the same sign as the middle term).

Algebra Activity Recording Sheet

(Use with the Lesson 9-2 Preview Activity on page 480 in the Student Edition.)

Factoring Using the Distributive Property

Materials: product mat, algebra tiles

Model and Analyze
Use algebra tiles to factor each binomial

1. $2x + 10$

2. $6x - 8$

3. $5x^2 + 2x$

4. $9 - 3x$

Tell whether each binomial can be factored. Justify your answer with a drawing.

5. $4x - 10$

6. $3x - 7$

7. $x^2 + 2x$

8. $2x^2 + 3$

Make a Conjecture
9. Write a paragraph that explains how you can use algebra tiles to determine whether a binomial can be factored. Include an example of one binomial that can be factored and one that cannot.

Using Overhead Manipulatives

(Use with Algebra 1, Lesson 9-2)

Factoring Using the Distributive Property

Objective Factor polynomials using algebra tiles.

Materials
- polynomial models transparency*
- algebra tiles*
- transparency pen*
- blank transparencies
- red and yellow acetate, if available

* = available in Overhead Manipulative Resources

Demonstration 1
Factoring $2x - 6$ and $2x^2 + 3x$

- Remind students that when you multiplied polynomials, you first constructed a rectangle using the factors as the width and length. You then covered the rectangle with algebra tiles to determine the product. Tell students they can reverse the process to find the factors of a polynomial.

- Display the polynomial models transparency and review the values of the algebra tiles.

- Write $2x - 6$ on a blank transparency. Ask students how to model this binomial using the tiles. **2 x tiles and 6 1 tiles**
  Model $2x - 6$ on top of the transparency.

- Tell students that if you can form a rectangle with these tiles, then you can find its width and length, and you will know the factors of the binomial. Ask students to form a rectangle using these tiles.

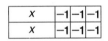

- Ask them to state the width and length of the rectangle.
  2, $x - 3$ Write the width and length next to the appropriate sides of the rectangle. Have them state the factors of $2x - 6$.
  2, $x - 3$ Write the factors on the transparency.

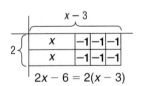

- Ask students how to factor $2x^2 + 3x$. **Build a rectangle with an area of $2x^2 + 3x$.** Place the tiles on the screen.

- Have students suggest ways to arrange the tiles into a rectangle. Try each suggestion until they arrive at the rectangle shown at the right.

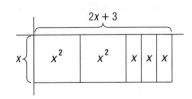

- Ask students to state the width and length of the rectangle.
  x, $2x + 3$ Have them state the factors of $2x^2 + 3x$. **x, $2x + 3$**
  Write $2x^2 + 3x = x(2x + 3)$ on the transparency.

(continued on the next page)

Demonstration 2
Factoring $2x^2 + 4xy$

- Use colored acetate to make 4 yellow xy tiles, or cut four rectangles out of a blank transparency and color them with a yellow transparency pen. (Make the x-dimension match the length of a 1 tile; make the y-dimension greater than the x-dimension.) Ask students how to model $2x^2 + 4xy$.
  2 x^2 tiles, 4 xy tiles

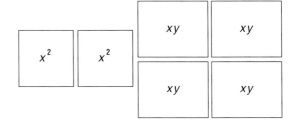

- Form the rectangle shown at the right. Ask students to name the width and length.
  x, $2x + 4xy$ Explain that $x(2x + 4xy)$ is not completely factored because each term on $2x + 4xy$ has a common factor, $2x$.

- Ask students if a different rectangle can be made from the tiles. Form the rectangle shown at the right. Have them state the width and length of the rectangle.
  2x, $x + 2y$
- Ask why $2x(x + 2y)$ is completely factored.
  There are no common factors in $x + 2y$.

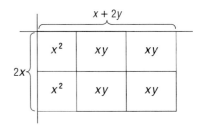

- Point out that in each of these examples one dimension of the rectangle involved only one kind of tile (1 tiles, x tiles, or y tiles), and a constant or variable was a factor in each term of the polynomial. Ask students how this information can help you factor using the Distributive Property.
  Look for factors common to each term.

Algebra Activity Recording Sheet

(Use with the Lesson 9-3 Preview Activity on pages 487–488 in the Student Edition.)

Factoring Trinomials

Materials: product mat, algebra tiles

Model
Use algebra tiles to factor each trinomial.

1. $x^2 + 4x + 3$

2. $x^2 + 5x + 4$

3. $x^2 - x - 6$

4. $x^2 - 3x + 2$

5. $x^2 + 7x + 12$

6. $x^2 - 4x + 4$

7. $x^2 - x - 2$

8. $x^2 - 6x + 8$

Using Overhead Manipulatives

(Use with Algebra 1, Lesson 9-3)

Factoring Trinomials

> **Objective** Factoring trinomials using algebra tiles.
>
> **Materials**
> - polynomial models tranparency*
> - algebra tiles*
> - transparency pen*
> - blank transperncies
> * = available in Overhead Manipulative Resources

Demonstration 1
Factoring $x^2 + 5x + 6$

- Tell students that you can use algebra tiles as a model for factoring trinomials. Remind them that when they used tiles to multiply binomials, the product was often a trinomial. Display the polynomial models transparency to review the guidelines for working with polynomial models.

- Ask students how to model $x^2 + 5x + 6$. **1 yellow x^2 tile, 5 yellow x tiles, and 6 yellow 1 tiles** Place a blank tranparency on the screen and model $x^2 + 5x + 6$ across the top.

- Tell students that one way to determine if a polynomial can be factored is if tiles representing the polynomial can be arranged into a rectangle.

- Move the x^2 tile to the center of the screen. Arrange the 6 1-tiles into a 2-by-3 rectangle as shown.

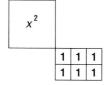

- Ask students to suggest ways to place the remaining x tiles to complete the rectangle.
- Have students state the width and length of the rectangle. **$x + 2$, $x + 3$** Ask them to state the factors of $x^2 + 5x + 6$. **$x + 2$, $x + 3$**

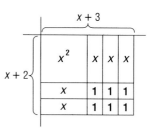

Demonstration 2
Factoring $x^2 + 3x - 4$

- Clear the screen. Ask students how to model the polynomial $x^2 + 3x - 4$. **1 yellow x^2 tile, 3 yellow *x* tiles, and 4 red 1 tiles** Place the tiles at the top of the screen.

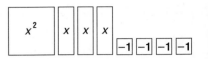

- Place the x^2 tile near the center of the screen. Arrange the 1 tiles into a 1 by 4 rectangular array as shown at the right.

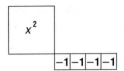

- Place the *x* tiles as shown.

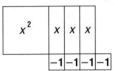

- Point out that the rectangle could be completed by adding two more *x* tiles. Remind students that you can add zero pairs of tiles without changing the value. Add a zero pair of *x* tiles as shown.

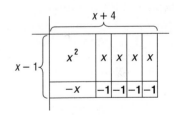

- Have students state the factors of $x^2 + 3x - 4$.
  $x - 1$, $x + 4$

- Ask whether you could have switched the positive and negative tiles of the zero pair and why. **No, there cannot be a negative 1 tile with a positive width and a positive length.**

Using Overhead Manipulatives

(Use with Algebra 1, Lesson 9-4)

Factoring Trinomials

Objective Factoring trinomials using algebra tiles.

Materials
- polynomial models transparency*
- algebra tiles*
- transparency pen*
- blank transparencies

* = available in Overhead Manipulative Resources

Demonstration
Factoring $2x^2 + 3x + 1$

- Ask students how to model the polynomial $2x^2 + 3x + 1$.
  2 yellow x^2 tiles, 3 yellow x tiles, and 1 yellow 1 tile
  Display the polynomial models transparency and place the
  tiles at the top of the screen.

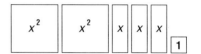

- Ask students to suggest ways to arrange the tiles into a
  rectangle. Try each suggestion until they arrive at the
  rectangle shown to the right.

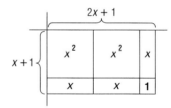

- Ask students to state the factors of $2x^2 + 3x + 1$.
  $x + 1, 2x + 1$

- Remind students that when you demonstrated how to factor
  $x^2 + 5x + 6$ and $x^2 + 3x - 4$, you first placed the x^2 tile(s)
  and the 1 tile(s). Then you looked for ways to fit the x tile(s)
  to make a rectangle. Ask students why this is similar to
  making an organized list of factors and their sum, as in the
  textbook. **When you arrange the x^2 tiles, you indicate the
  factor of the coefficient of the first term; when you arrange
  the 1 tiles, you indicate the factors of the last term. To fit the
  x tile(s), you are looking for a sum of those factors that
  matches the number of x tiles.**

NAME _____ DATE _____ PERIOD _____

Algebra Activity Transparency

(Use with Algebra 1, Lesson 9-4)

Factoring Trinomials

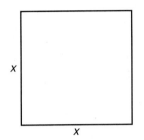

Area = _____

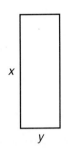

Area = _____

Area = _____

Figure 1

$x^2 + xy$

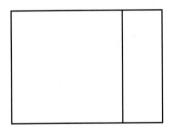

Length = _____

Width = _____

Figure 2

$x^2 + 2xy + y^2$

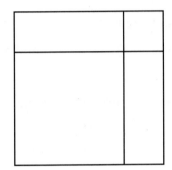

Length = _____

Width = _____

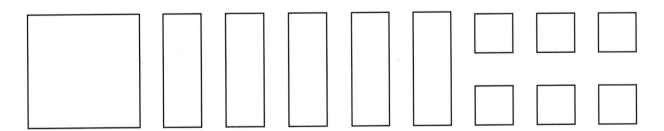

163

Teaching Algebra with Manipulatives

Algebra Activity

(Use with Algebra 1, Lesson 9-4)

Factoring Trinomials

$$x^2 + 5xy + 6y^2$$

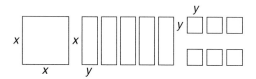

1. Use algebra tiles to form one rectangle. Draw a picture of your rectangle below.

2. How long is your rectangle?_____ How wide is it?_____

3. What do you think the length and width of the rectangle represent?

   _____

4. Repeat the above procedure using the following polynomials and find the dimensions of the rectangles.

   a. $2x^2 + 3xy + y^2$ _____

   b. $x^2 + 3xy + 2y^2$ _____

5. What conclusion can you draw regarding the dimensions of the rectangles?

164

Using Overhead Manipulatives

(Use with Algebra 1, Lesson 9-5)

Factoring Differences of Squares

Objective Factoring the differences of squares using algebra tiles.

Materials
- algebra tiles*
- transparency pens*
- straightedge
- blank transparencies
- colored acetate, if available

* = available in Overhead Manipulative Resources

Demonstration
Factoring the Difference of Squares

- On a blank transparency, draw a line segment 4 inches long. Label this segment a. Construct an a by a square. Ask students to find the area of the square. a^2

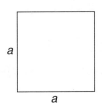

- Draw another line segment 1.5 inches long. Label this segment b. Construct a b by b square. Have students find the area of the smaller square. b^2

- Place the small square inside the large square and shade the L-shaped part of the square as shown. Ask students to state an algebraic expression for the area of the shaded part. $a^2 - b^2$ Point out that this expression is called the **difference of squares**.

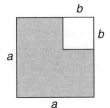

- Ask students what the length of the top of the L is. $a - b$ Ask what the length of the right side of L is. $a - b$ Erase the unshaded portion of the figure, and label the edges with length b as shown. Then draw a dashed line to separate the L into two regions as shown.

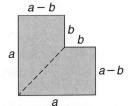

- Place a blank transparency on top of the figure. Trace the figure and the dashed line. Cut out the figure and cut along the dashed line to form two trapezoids. Rearrange the trapezoids to form the rectangle shown. Label the edges.

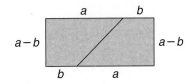

- Ask them to state the width of the rectangle. **$a - b$** Have students state the length of the rectangle. **$a + b$**

- Ask students to state an expression for the area of the rectangle. **$(a - b)(a + b)$** Point out that the area of the L-shaped figure is $a^2 - b^2$, so the expressions have the same value. Write $a^2 - b^2 = (a - b)(a + b)$ below the rectangle.

- Have students describe the factors of the difference of two squares. **One factor is the sum of the square roots of the terms; the other is the difference of the square roots of the terms.**

Extension
Factoring the Difference of Squares Using Algebra Tiles

- Tell students that you can use algebra tiles to factor the differences of squares. Place a positive x^2 tile and a negative y^2 tile on top of a blank tranparency as shown. Point out that these tiles represent the difference of squares, $x^2 - y^2$.

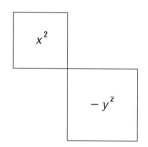

- Ask students what would be needed to form a square from the tiles. **2 *xy* tiles** Remind students that you can add a zero pair of tiles without affecting the value of what is shown. Place a zero pair of xy tiles on the screen to complete the square.

- Label the sides of the square as shown. Ask students to state the factors of $x^2 - y^2$. **$x - y$, $x + y$** Write $x^2 - y^2 = (x - y)(x + y)$ below the square. Ask students if this matches the description they gave at the end of the previous demonstration. **yes**

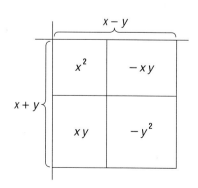

Algebra Activity Recording Sheet

(Use with the activity on page 501 in Lesson 9-5 of the Student Edition.)

Difference of Squares

Materials: straightedge, scissors

Make a Conjecture

1. Write an expression representing the area of the rectangle.

2. Explain why $a^2 - b^2 = (a + b)(a - b)$.

Using Overhead Manipulatives

(Use with Algebra 1, Lesson 9-6)

Factoring Perfect Square Trinomials

Objective Factor perfect square trinomials using algebra tiles.

Materials
- polynomial models transparency*
- algebra tiles*
- transparency pen*
- blank transparencies

* = available in Overhead Manipulative Resources

Demonstration 1
Factoring $x^2 - 2x + 1$

- Use the polynomial models transparency to review the guidelines for working with polynomial models.

- Tell students that a trinomial is a perfect square if it can be modeled with algebra tiles to form a square, without adding any zero pairs.

- Have students model $x^2 - 2x + 1$ with the algebra tiles.

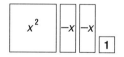

- Ask them to form a square using these tiles. Label the length and width as shown. Ask students why the model correctly shows $(x - 1)(x - 1)$. **$(x)(x) = x^2$, $(x)(-1) = -x$, $(-1)(x) = -x$, $(-1)(-1) = 1$; $x^2 + (-x) + (-x) + 1 = x^2 - 2x + 1$**

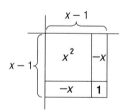

- Have students state the factors of $x^2 - 2x + 1$. **$x - 1, x - 1$**

Demonstration 2
Factoring $x^2 + 4x + 4$

- Ask students to model $x^2 + 4x + 4$.

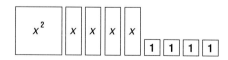

- Have them form a square using these tiles. Ask students to label the length and width of the square. **$x + 2, x + 2$**

- Ask students to state the factors of $x^2 + 4x + 4$. **$x + 2, x + 2$** Have them check the product of the factors by using the FOIL method.

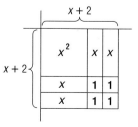

Demonstration 2
Factoring $4x^2 - 4x + 1$

- Have students model $4x^2 - 4x + 1$.

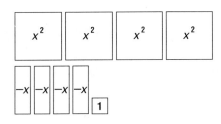

- Ask students to form a square using these tiles.
- Ask them what the length and width are. **$2x - 1$, $2x - 1$**
- Have them state the factors of $4x^2 - 4x + 1$. **$2x - 1$, $2x - 1$** Have them check the product of the factors by using the FOIL method.

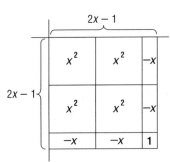

Extension
Analyzing Perfect Square Trinomials

- Ask students what was true about the x^2-tiles and the 1-tiles in each demonstration. **They formed squares.**

- Ask what this means about the first and last term of these trinomials. **They are perfect squares.**

- Ask if those terms can ever be negative in a perfect square trinomial, and why. **No, any number squared is always positive.** Point out that the middle term could be either positive or negative.

- Ask whether $2x^2 - 2x + 4$ is a perfect square trinomial and why. **No, the first term is not a perfect square.**

Mini-Project

(Use with Algebra 1, Lesson 9-6)

Factoring Trinomial Squares

Use $\boxed{x^2}$, $\boxed{x}$, **and** $\boxed{1}$ **to represent** x^2, x, **and 1, respectively.**

Use the models to represent the trinomial $x^2 + 4x + 4$.

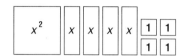

Arrange the models to form a rectangle.

x	1	1
x	1	1
x^2	x	x

1. What do you notice about the length and width of the final rectangle?

2. Give the dimensions of the final rectangle. (The dimensions are the factors of the trinomial.)

Factor each of the following polynomials by forming rectangular regions with the models.

3. $x^2 + 6x + 9$

4. $4x^2 + 4x + 1$

5. $x^2 + 4x + 3$

6. $x^2 + 2x + 1$

7. $x^2 + 8x + 16$

8. $3x^2 + 4x + 1$

9. Which of the rectangles above are squares?

10. What do you call a trinomial whose representation is square?

11. How can you tell whether a trinomial is a perfect square trinomial?

12. Factor $x^2 - 4$ by forming a rectangular region from two trapezoids.

Teaching Algebra with Manipulatives

Quadratic and Exponential Functions
Teaching Notes and Overview

Algebra Activity
Recording Sheet
Symmetry of Parabolas
(p. 176 of this booklet)

Use With the activity on page 525 in Lesson 10-1 of the Student Edition.

Objective Graph, fold, and analyze the symmetry of a parabola.

Materials
grid paper

Form groups of two students for this activity. Before working the exercises, have them read Steps 1 through 3. Make sure students know how to set-up a table and find ordered pairs that satisfy a quadratic function. To determine if, and where, the curve crosses the y-axis, tell students to substitute $x = 0$ and solve for y (y-intercept). As soon as they complete the model, ask students to answer the questions in Exercises 1 through 4. Discuss the answers to the questions. Have each group read their answer to Exercise 4.

Answers
See Teacher Wraparound Edition p. 525.

Mini-Project
Graphing Quadratic Functions
(p. 177 of this booklet)

Use With Lesson 10-1.

Objective Graph and analyze a quadratic function.

Divide students into groups of two or three. Have a student read the problem. Ask questions about the problem to check their understanding. Be sure that they understand what t and h represent in the quadratic function. Have students begin Exercise 1 of the Mini-Project by finding values for h, when whole-numbered values are substituted for t. Students should notice that the highest point (maximum point) is between the points (3, 198) and (4, 198). If $t = 3.5$, then $h = 202$. The vertex of the parabola is (3.5, 202) and the maximum height is 202 feet.

Check students' graphs. When students are finished, discuss Exercises 3 and 4.

Answers

1. Sample values: (0, 6), (1, 102), (2, 166), (3, 198), (4, 198), (5, 166), (6, 102), (7, 6), (8, 774)

2. See students' graphs.

3. The maximum height is 202 feet. The maximum height is at the vertex of the graph, which is at (3.5, 202).

Using Overhead
Manipulatives
Solving Quadratic Equations by Completing the Square
(pp. 178–179 of this booklet)

Use With Lesson 10-3.

Objective Model and solve quadratic equations using algebra tiles.

Materials
algebra tiles*
equation mat transparency*
transparency pen*
* = available in Overhead Manipulative Resources

This demonstration contains one activity dealing with solving a quadratic equation by completing the square. On an equation mat, $x^2 + 4x - 5 = -3$ is modeled with algebra tiles. The part $x^2 + 4x - 5$ is identified as not being a perfect square. Therefore, it is necessary to form zero pairs of tiles to make a perfect square. Five positive zero pairs are added to each side without affecting the value of the equation. Then students are lead to see that it is necessary to arrange tiles on the left side to begin to form a square. To finish the square, 4 positive 1-tiles are needed. These are added to each side. The left side $x^2 + 4x + 4$ factored is $(x + 2)^2$. Now the equation modeled on the mat is $(x + 2)^2 = 6$. Next, the solution set is explained. The same procedure is used to model and solve $x^2 - 2x + 3 = 6$.

Answers
Answers appear on the teacher demonstration instructions on pages 178–179.

Algebra Activity
A Fascinating Fold
(p. 180 of this booklet)

Use With Lesson 10-5.

Objective Investigate a relationship between certain exponential functions.

Materials
grid paper
straightedge

Do this activity with the whole class. Go over the general plan of the Algebra Activity. Next, have students complete the table for the three functions in Step 1. Then ask them to prepare the grid paper as stated in the directions for Step 2 and graph $y = 2^x$.

In Step 3, have them fold the grid paper along the y-axis of the graph $y = 2^x$. Mark the points from $y = 2^x$ onto Quadrant II. Unfold the paper and connect the points with a smooth curve. At this time, you may want to review how to evaluate an expression like $\left(\dfrac{1}{2}\right)^{-3}$, that is, 8.

Point out that the reflection of the point $(3, 8)$ from $y = 2^x$ over the y-axis is $(-3, 8)$ from $y = \left(\dfrac{1}{2}\right)^x$. Ask students to complete the table for $y = \left(\dfrac{1}{2}\right)^x$. Before students begin Exercises 1–3, they should realize that they are finding the reflections of $y = 3^x$ and $y = 4^x$ over the y-axis and writing a paragraph describing any discoveries they made from doing the activity. Interested students may want to investigate negative values for x for $y = 2^x$ and other exponential functions, and share their findings with the rest of the class.

Step 1

x	2^x	$(x, 2^x)$	3^x	$(x, 3^x)$	4^x	$(x, 4^x)$
0	1	(0, 1)	1	(0, 1)	1	(0, 1)
1	2	(1, 2)	3	(1, 3)	4	(1, 4)
2	4	(2, 4)	9	(2, 9)	16	(2, 16)
3	8	(3, 8)	27	(3, 27)	64	(3, 64)
4	16	(4, 16)	81	(4, 81)	256	(4, 256)
5	32	(5, 32)	243	(5, 243)		
6	64	(6, 64)				

Step 2

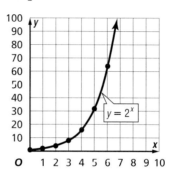

Step 3

x	$\left(\dfrac{1}{2}\right)^x$	$\left(x, \left(\dfrac{1}{2}\right)^x\right)$
0	1	(0, 1)
−1	2	(−1, 2)
−2	4	(−2, 4)
−3	8	(−3, 8)
−4	16	(−4, 16)
−5	32	(−5, 32)
−6	64	(−6, 64)

Answers

1. $y = \left(\dfrac{1}{3}\right)^x$ 2. $y = \left(\dfrac{1}{4}\right)^x$

3. Sample answer: All of the functions in this activity have a common point, (0, 1). When you compare a function and its reflection over the y-axis, the constants that are raised to a power are reciprocals. So the reflection

of $y = 2^x$ is $y = \left(\frac{1}{2}\right)^x$. The reflection of $y = 3^x$ is $y = \left(\frac{1}{3}\right)^x$, and so on.

and (3, 100). Ask students to complete the table and Exercises 1–6 in small groups. Discuss the work. Some students may want to do further investigations on the Richter scale by using the INTERNET.

Answers
See Teacher Wraparound Edition p. 573.

Algebra Activity Recording Sheet

Graphs of Geometric Sequences
(p. 181 of this booklet)

Use With the activity on page 569 in Lesson 10-7 of the Student Edition.

Objective Graph geometric sequences and compare them to exponential functions.

Materials
grid paper

Students will graph geometric sequences. Then they will compare the graphs to an exponential function. Finally, they will compare the formula for an exponential function to the value of the nth term of a geometric sequence.

Answers
See Teacher Wraparound Edition p. 569.

Algebra Activity Recording Sheet

Investigating Rates of Change
(p. 182 of this booklet)

Use With Lesson 10-7 as a follow-up activity. This corresponds to the activity on page 573 in the Student Edition.

Objective Investigating rates of change by graphing and analyzing the data, making a conjecture and extending the investigation.

Materials
grid paper

Point out that the Richter scale is used to measure the force of an earthquake. Students are asked in Step 1 to plot on grid paper the ordered pairs (Rich Number, Increase in Magnitude). In Step 2, explain how the rate of change from one value to the next is found. Have them find the rate of change for (2, 10)

Algebra Activity Recording Sheet

(Use with the activity on page 525 in Lesson 10-1 of the Student Edition.)

Symmetry of Parabolas

Materials: grid paper

Make a Conjecture

1. What is the vertex of the parabola?

2. Write an equation of the fold line.

3. Which point on the parabola lies on the fold line?

4. Write a few sentences to describe the symmetry of a parabola based on your findings in this activity.

Mini-Project

(Use with Algebra 1, Lesson 10-1)

Graphing Quadratic Functions

A ball is thrown vertically into the air with a velocity of 112 feet per second. The ball was released 6 feet above the ground. The height above the ground t seconds after release is given by the formula $h = -16t^2 + 112t + 6$.

1. Complete the table using whole-number values for t.

t	h

2. Use the values in the table to graph the equation representing the height of the ball.

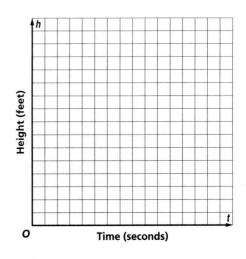

3. What is the maximum height the ball achieves? Explain how you know.

4. How long did it take the ball to return to the ground?

Algebra 1—Chapter 10

Using Overhead Manipulatives

(Use with Algebra 1, Lesson 10-3)

Solving Quadratic Equations by Completing the Square

Objective Use algebra tiles to solve quadratic equations by completing the square.

Materials
- equation mat transparency*
- algebra tiles*
- transparency pen*   * = available in Overhead Manipulative Resources

Demonstration
Solve $x^2 + 4x - 5 = -3$.

- Place tiles on the equation mat transparency to model $x^2 + 4x - 5 = -3$. Write $x^2 + 4x - 5 = -3$ on the transparency.

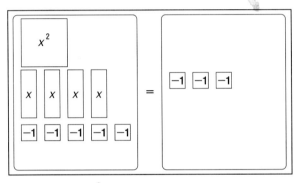

$$x^2 + 4x - 5 = -3$$

- Point out to students that $x^2 + 4x - 5$ is not a perfect square. Tell students that zero pairs of tiles are formed when a positive tile is paired with a negative tile of the same size and shape. Ask students what you might do to remove the negative 1 tiles from the left side of the mat without affecting the value of the equation. **Add 5 positive 1 tiles to each side** Add 5 yellow 1 tiles to each side and remove the zero pairs.

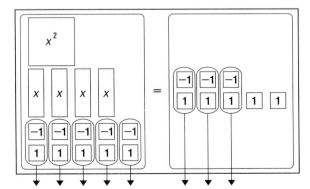

- Arrange the tiles on the left side of the mat to start to form a square.

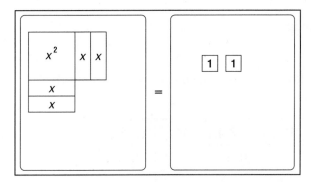

- Ask students what must be added to each side of the mat so that a square is formed on the left side. **4 yellow 1 tiles** Add 4 yellow 1 tiles to each side.

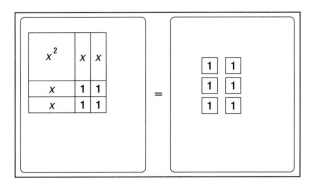

- Ask students to state the expression for the square on the left side of the mat. $x^2 + 4x + 4$ Remind students that when they used models to factor perfect square trinomials, the length of each side of the square represented the factors of the trinomial. Have students factor $x^2 + 4x + 4$. $(x + 2)^2$

- Tell students to write the equation that is now modeled on the mat. $(x + 2)^2 = 6$ Have them find the square root of each side of the equation and then find the solution set. $x + 2 = \pm\sqrt{6}$; $\{\sqrt{6} - 2, -\sqrt{6} - 2\}$

- Have students repeat the same procedure for solving $x^2 - 2x + 3 = 6$. Ask students to state the solution set for $x^2 - 2x + 3 = 6$. $\{-1, 3\}$

Algebra Activity

(Use with Algebra 1, Lesson 10-5)

A Fascinating Fold

Materials: grid paper, straightedge

Collect the Data

Step 1   Complete the table below for these three different exponential functions.

x	2^x	$(x, 2^x)$	3^x	$(x, 3^x)$	4^x	$(x, 4^x)$
0	$2^0 = 1$	$(0, 1)$	$3^0 = 1$	$(0, 1)$	$4^0 = 1$	$(0, 1)$
1						
2						
3						
4						
5						
6						

Step 2   Place $(0, 0)$ near the bottom and the center of a sheet of grid paper. Label the x-axis by units of one and the y-axis by units of ten. Graph $y = 2^x$ by plotting the ordered pairs in Column 3 and connecting the points with a smooth curve.

Step 3   Fold the grid paper along the y-axis and hold it up to a window. Mark the points from $y = 2^x$ onto Quadrant II. Unfold the paper and connect the points with a smooth curve. The function in Quadrant II is the exponential function $y = \left(\dfrac{1}{2}\right)^x$.

Use your graph and the table from Step 1 to finish the table at the right.

x	$\left(\dfrac{1}{2}\right)^x$	$\left(x, \left(\dfrac{1}{2}\right)^x\right)$
0	$\left(\dfrac{1}{2}\right)^0 = 1$	$(0, 1)$
−1	$\left(\dfrac{1}{2}\right)^{-1} = 2$	$(-1, 2)$
−2		
−3		
−4		
−5		
−6		

Analyze the Data

1. Repeat Steps 2 and 3 for $y = 3^x$. What is the equation of the function in Quadrant II?

2. Repeat Steps 2 and 3 for $y = 4^x$. What is the equation of the function in Quadrant II?

3. Write a paragraph describing any discoveries you made in this activity.

Algebra Activity Recording Sheet

(Use with the activity on page 569 in Lesson 10-7 of the Student Edition.)

Graphs of Geometric Sequences

Materials: grid paper

Model

Use grid paper to graph each geometric sequence. Name each common ratio.

1. 1, 2, 4, 8, 16,...

2. 1, −2, 4, −8, 16,...

3. 81, 27, 9, 3, 1,...

4. −81, 27, −9, 3, −1,...

5. 0.2, 1, 5, 25, 125,...

6. −0.2, 1, −5, 25, −125,...

Analyze

7. Which graphs appear to be similar to an exponential function?

8. Compare and contrast the graph of geometric sequences with $r > 0$ and $r < 0$.

9. Compare the formula for an exponential function $y = c(a^x)$ to the value of the nth term of a geometric sequence.

Teaching Algebra with Manipulatives

Algebra 1—Chapter 10

Algebra Activity Recording Sheet

(Use with the Lesson 10-7 Follow-Up Activity on page 573 in the Student Edition.)

Investigating Rates of Change

Materials: grid paper

Analyze the Data

1. Describe the graph you made of the Richter scale data.

2. Is the rate of change between any two points the same?

Make a Conjecture

3. Can the data be represented by a linear equation? Why or why not?

4. Describe the pattern shown in the rates of change in Column 3.

Extend the Investigation

5. Use a graphing calculator or graphing software to find a regression equation for the Richter scale data. (*Hint*: If you are using the TI-83 Plus, use ExpReg.)

6. Graph the following set of data that shows the amount of energy released for each Richter scale value. Describe the graph. Fill in the third column and describe the rates of change. Find a regression equation for this set of data. If necessary, write your answers on the back of this sheet.

Richter Number (x)	Energy Released (y)	Rate of Change (slope)
1	0.00017 metric ton	
2	0.006 metric ton	
3	0.179 metric ton	
4	5 metric tons	
5	179 metric tons	
6	5643 metric tons	
7	179,100 metric tons	

Source: *The New York Public Library Science Desk Reference*

Radical Expressions and Triangles
Teaching Notes and Overview

Mini-Project
Matching Radicals
(p. 185 of this booklet)

Use With Lesson 11-2.

Objective Simplify radical expressions.

Materials
scissors

This activity requires students to work in pairs to simplify radical expressions that can be simplified. Have them write the simplification in that box and circle it. Then have them cut out the rectangles and match the ones that are equivalent expressions.

Answers
A, J; B, L; C, I; D, E; E, D; F, N; G, P; H, O; I, C; J, A; K, M; L, B; M, K; N, F; O, H; P, G

Using Overhead Manipulatives
The Pythagorean Theorem
(p. 186 of this booklet)

Use With Lesson 11-4.

Objective Explore the relationships in a right triangle and discover the Pythagorean Theorem.

Materials
dot paper transparency*
transparency pen*
* = available in Overhead Manipulative Resources

On a dot paper transparency a right triangle is drawn. Squares are drawn on all three sides. Each side of each square is as long as the corresponding side of the triangle. The areas of the two smaller squares are found. The area of the large square requires the use of Pick's Theorem. Students are guided to discover the Pythagorean Theorem.

Answers
Answers appear on the teacher demonstration instructions on page 186.

Algebra Activity
The Pythagorean Theorem
(pp. 187–188 of this booklet)

Use With Lesson 11-4.

Objective Determine whether a triangle is a right triangle, given the lengths of its sides.

Materials
classroom set of Algebra Activity worksheets
transparency master of Algebra Activity
calculator
grid paper
scissors*
* = available in Overhead Manipulative Resources

Prior to class, you may want to cut the transparency on the dashed lines. Using the individual squares, explain that the area of each large square equals the length of one of its sides squared.

Form a right triangle using the sides from each square as its legs. As soon as the groups have completed Exercises 1 and 2, ask them what they learned from completing these exercises. Discuss the relationship between the sides of a right triangle.

Discuss the answers to Exercises 3 and 4. Point out that squares of three numbers that satisfy the Pythagorean Theorem are called Pythagorean triples. Some students may want to find additional Pythagorean triples. Let students use a calculator to work Exercise 5.

Answers

1. 9, 16, 25; $9 + 16 = 25$ or $3^2 + 4^2 = 5^2$

2. right triangle; $a^2 + b^2 = c^2$

3. 1, 4, 9, 16, 25, 36, 49, 64, 81, 100, 121, 144, 169, 196, 225, 256, 289, 324, 361, 400, 441, 484, 529, 576, 625, 676, 729, 784, 841, 900

4. 3, 4, 5; 5, 12, 13; 6, 8, 10; 7, 24, 25; 8, 15, 17; 9, 12, 15; 10, 24, 26; 12, 16, 20; 15, 20, 25; 18, 24, 30; 20, 21, 29

5a. 39 ft   **5b.** 12.5 m   **5c.** $\sqrt{145}$ in. ≈ 12 in.

Teaching Algebra with Manipulatives

 ## Using Overhead Manipulatives

Graphing Irrational Numbers
(p. 189 of this booklet)
Use With Lesson 11-4.

Objective Use the Pythagorean Theorem to graph irrational numbers.

Materials
compass   centimeter grid transparency*
straightedge   transparency pens*
* = available in Overhead Manipulative Resources

Students apply the Pythagorean Theorem to graph an irrational number. Ask students to follow along. It is important that students estimate the value of $\sqrt{13}$.

Answers
Answers appear on page 189.

 ## Using Overhead Manipulatives

Similar Triangles (p. 190 of this booklet)
Use With Lesson 11-6.

Objective Discover that corresponding angles of similar triangles are congruent and corresponding sides of similar triangles are proportional.

Materials
protractor*   transparency pens*
centimeter ruler*   blank transparency
* = available in Overhead Manipulative Resources

This demonstration deals with projecting a triangle on a transparency with lengths of 6 cm, 15 cm, and 12 cm. The triangle is traced with the lengths of the sides labeled. Next, the projector with the same transparency is moved to the left and back until the projected image of the side lengths are 8 cm, 20 cm, and 16 cm long. This triangle is traced and labeled. Students compare the measures of the corresponding angles and compare the ratios of the measures of the corresponding sides.

Answers
Answers appear on page 190.

 ## Algebra Activity Recording Sheet

Investigating Trigonometric Ratios
(p. 191 of this booklet)
Use With Lesson 11-7 as a preview activity. This corresponds with page 622 of the Student Edition.

Objective Make and use paper triangles to investigate trigonometric ratios.

Materials
ruler   grid paper   protractor

Students make right triangles whose legs are in a 7:10 ratio. They measure and record the lengths of the sides of each triangle, as well as the ratio between them. The measures of all the angles are also recorded. Finally, students examine their table of measures and ratios to identify and describe the patterns they see.

Answers
See Teacher Wraparound Edition p. 622.

Algebra Activity Recording Sheet

Make a Hypsometer (p. 192 of this booklet)
Use With the activity on page 626 in Lesson 11-7 of the Student Edition.

Objective Make and use a hypsometer to measure a large object that cannot be measured directly.

Materials
piece of string   protractor   straw
tall object outside   paper clip   yardstick

Students use the materials listed to make a hypsometer. Then they find an object outside that is too tall to be measured directly. They find the height by using the tangent formula, the angle of elevation, the distance from the ground to the student's eye level, and the distance of the object from the student.

Answers
See Teacher Wraparound Edition p. 626.

Mini-Project

(Use with Algebra 1, Lesson 11-2)

Matching Radicals

Work in pairs. Simplify each radical expression that can be simplified. Then cut out the rectangles, and match each one to another equivalent expression. If you do this correctly, each rectangle will match one and only one rectangle.

A	B	C	D
$(5 + \sqrt{2})(5 - \sqrt{2})$	$9\sqrt{3}$	$\sqrt{3}(\sqrt{6} + 2\sqrt{21})$	$20\sqrt{6}$
			$2\sqrt{30}$
$\sqrt{45} + \sqrt{80}$	62	$\sqrt{529}$	$2\sqrt{22}$
E	**F**	**G**	**H**
$5\sqrt{3} \cdot \sqrt{32}$	$\sqrt{169}$	$7\sqrt{5}$	$\sqrt{81a^2b^4}$
$\sqrt{12} \cdot \sqrt{10}$	$5\sqrt{3} + \sqrt{27} - \sqrt{48}$	$10\sqrt{30}$	$\sqrt{99}$
$\sqrt{88}$	$\sqrt{100a^4b^3}$	$8\sqrt{3} - 2\sqrt{15}$	$16\sqrt{45} - 3\sqrt{20}$
I	**J**	**K**	**L**
$3\sqrt{2} + 6\sqrt{7}$	23	$10a^2b^2$	$\sqrt{243}$
23	$7\sqrt{5}$	$3|a|b^2\sqrt{7}$	$(8 + \sqrt{2})(8 - \sqrt{2})$
M	**N**	**O**	**P**
$\sqrt{100a^4b^4}$	13	$9|a|b^2$	$\sqrt{245}$
	$4\sqrt{3}$	$3\sqrt{11}$	$\sqrt{3000}$
$\sqrt{63a^2b^4}$	$10a^2|b|\sqrt{b}$	$42\sqrt{5}$	$\sqrt{6}(4\sqrt{2} - \sqrt{10})$

Algebra 1—Chapter 11

185

Using Overhead Manipulatives

(Use with Algebra 1, Lesson 11-4)

The Pythagorean Theorem

> **Objective** Explore the relationships in a right triangle and discover the Pythagorean Theorem.
>
> **Materials**
> - dot paper transparency*
> - transparency pen*
>
> * = available in Overhead Manipulative Resources

Demonstration
The Pythagorean Theorem

- Draw a triangle as shown at the right. Ask students why it is called a right triangle. **It contains one right angle.**

- Using the longest side of the triangle, draw a square. Point out to students that the side of the square has the same length as the longest side of the triangle.

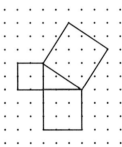

- Draw squares on the two shorter sides of triangle. Point out to students that the length of the side of each square is the length of the corresponding side of the triangle.

- Ask students to find the area of each of the two smaller squares. **4 units² ; 9 units²**

- Tell students they can find the area of the large square by using Pick's Theorem. Pick's Theorem is $A = \frac{x}{2} + y - 1$, where x represents the number of dots on the sides of the figure and y represents the number of dots inside the figure. Have students find the area of the largest square using Pick's Theorem. **13 units²**

- Ask students to compare the areas of three squares. **The sum of the areas of the two smaller squares equals the area of the largest square.**

- Have students describe the relationship between the lengths of the three sides of the right triangle. **The sum of the squares of the lengths of the two shortest sides is equal to the square of the longest side.** At this time name the sides of a right triangle. In a right triangle, the side opposite the right angle is called the *hypotenuse* and the other two sides are called the *legs* of the triangle.

- Inform students that this relationship is called the Pythagorean Theorem.

Extension

- Ask students to use the work-backward strategy and Pick's Theorem to draw a square with an area of 18 units². **Draw a right triangle with each leg 3 units long. The square on the hypotenuse has an area of 18 units².**

Algebra Activity Transparency Master
(Use with Algebra 1, Lesson 11-4)

The Pythagorean Theorem

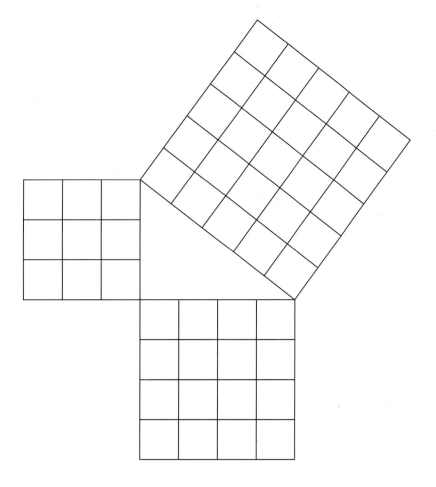

Algebra Activity

(Use with Algebra 1, Lesson 11-4)

The Pythagorean Theorem

1. Cut three squares from graph paper with sides of length 3, 4, and 5. What is the area of each square?

   Write an equation to show that the sum of the areas of two of the squares is equal to the area of the third square.

2. Place the three squares on a sheet of paper so that their sides form a triangle. What type of triangle is it?

   Write an equation to show the relationship among the squares of the sides of the triangle. Let a and b represent the length of the legs and c the length of the hypotenuse.

3. Find the squares of the numbers from 1 to 30. Use your calculator.

$1^2 =$ _____	$7^2 =$ _____	$13^2 =$ _____	$19^2 =$ _____	$25^2 =$ _____
$2^2 =$ _____	$8^2 =$ _____	$14^2 =$ _____	$20^2 =$ _____	$26^2 =$ _____
$3^2 =$ _____	$9^2 =$ _____	$15^2 =$ _____	$21^2 =$ _____	$27^2 =$ _____
$4^2 =$ _____	$10^2 =$ _____	$16^2 =$ _____	$22^2 =$ _____	$28^2 =$ _____
$5^2 =$ _____	$11^2 =$ _____	$17^2 =$ _____	$23^2 =$ _____	$29^2 =$ _____
$6^2 =$ _____	$12^2 =$ _____	$18^2 =$ _____	$24^2 =$ _____	$30^2 =$ _____

4. Find four sets of three squares each such that the sum of two of the squares equals the third.

   _____   _____

   _____   _____

5. Find the length of the hypotenuse of the right triangle given the lengths of its other sides. Use a calculator.

   a. 15 feet, 36 feet _____

   b. 7.5 meters, 10 meters _____

   c. 8 inches, 9 inches _____

Using Overhead Manipulatives

(Use with Algebra 1, Lesson 11-4)

Graphing Irrational Numbers

Objective Use the Pythagorean Theorem to graph irrational numbers.

Materials
- compass
- straightedge
- centimeter grid transparency*
- transparency pens*

* = available in Overhead Manipulative Resources

Demonstration
Graphing the Irrational Number $\sqrt{13}$

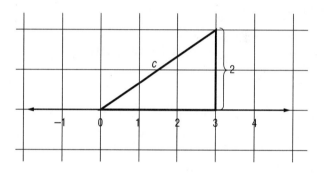

- Tell students that graphing an irrational number requires the construction of a right triangle having a side of length equal to the length you wish to graph. Ask students to consider the following method for graphing $\sqrt{13}$.

- Have students express 13 as the sum of two squares. $13 = 2^2 + 3^2$

- Draw a number line on the centimeter grid transparency. At 3, construct a perpendicular segment 2 units long.

- Use a different color to draw the hypotenuse. Label it c.

- Using the Pythagorean Theorem, replace a with 2 and b with 3 to show that c is $\sqrt{13}$.

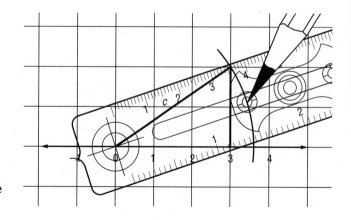

- Open the compass to the length of the hypotenuse. With the compass at 0, draw an arc that intersects the number line. Label the intersection B. The distance from 0 to B is $\sqrt{13}$ units.

- Estimate the value of $\sqrt{13}$ based on the graph. Check using a calculator.

Extension

- Have students explain how to graph $\sqrt{12}$. *Hint*: Think of 12 as $4^2 - 2^2$. **On a number line, draw a perpendicular 4 units long at 2. Draw the hypotenuse and label the perpendicular leg *a*. Set the compass to the length of *a*. With the compass at 0, draw an arc that intersects the number line. Label the distance *D*. The distance from 0 to *D* is $\sqrt{12}$.**

Teaching Algebra with Manipulatives

Using Overhead Manipulatives

(Use with Algebra 1, Lesson 11-6)

Similar Triangles

> **Objective** Discover that corresponding angles of similar triangles are congruent and corresponding sides of similar triangles are proportional.
>
> **Materials**
> - protractor*
> - centimeter ruler*
> - transparency pens*
> - blank transparency
>
> * = available in Overhead Manipulative Resources

Demonstration
Similar Triangles

- Draw a triangle with side lengths of 6 cm, 15 cm, and 12 cm on a blank transparency. Display the triangle on the chalkboard or white board.

- Ask a pair of students to move the projector and determine how far from the board the projector must be to obtain a triangle with sides 6 cm, 15 cm, and 12 cm long. Have one of the students trace that triangle.

- Ask another pair of students to move the projector to the left and back until the side lengths of the projected image are 8 cm, 20 cm, and 16 cm long. Have one of the students trace that triangle.

- Have students compare the measures of the corresponding angles and compare the ratios of the measures of the corresponding sides. **The corresponding angles are congruent and the corresponding sides form equal ratios.**

- Ask students to repeat the activity with a different initial triangle, moving the projector back the same distance but to the right. Have students explain their findings. **The findings are the same.**

Algebra Activity Recording Sheet

(Use with the Lesson 11-7 Preview Activity on page 622 in the Student Edition.)

Investigating Trigonometric Ratios

Materials: ruler, grid paper, protractor

Collect the Data
Use the table to record your data.

Side Lengths			Ratios		Angle Measures		
side $\overline{BC}$	side $\overline{AC}$	side $\overline{AB}$	BC:AC	BC:AB	angle A	angle B	angle C
3.5	5						90°
7	10						90°
14	20						90°
							90°
							90°
							90°

Analyze the Data
1. Examine the measures and ratios in the table. What do you notice? Write a sentence or two to describe any patterns you see.

Make a Conjecture
2. For any right triangle similar to the ones you have drawn here, what will be the value of the ratio of the length of the shortest leg to the length of the longest leg?

3. If you draw a right triangle and calculate the ratio of the length of the shortest leg to the length of the hypotenuse to be approximately 0.573, what will be the measure of the larger acute angle in the right triangle?

Algebra Activity Recording Sheet

(Use with the activity on page 626 in Lesson 11-7 of the Student Edition.)

Make a Hypsometer

Materials: piece of string, straw, paper clip, protractor, tall object outside, yardstick

Analyze

1. Make a sketch of your measurements. Use the equation tan (angle of elevation) $= \dfrac{\text{height of object} - x}{\text{distance of object}}$, where x represents distance from the ground to your eye level, to find the height of the object.

2. Why do you have to subtract the angle measurement on the hypsometer from 90° to find the angle of elevation?

3. Compare your answer with someone who measured the same object. Did your heights agree? Why or why not?

12

Rational Expressions and Equations
Teaching Notes and Overview

Using Overhead Manipulatives

Dividing Polynomials by Monomials and by Binomials
(pp. 195–196 of this booklet)

Use With Lesson 12-5.

Objective Dividing polynomials by monomials and by binomials using algebra tiles.

Materials
algebra tiles*
product mat transparency*
transparency pen*
blank transparencies
* = available in Overhead Manipulative Resources

This demonstration contains two activities. Both activities use algebra tiles and the area of a rectangle to model dividing polynomials. Students need to know what the 1 tile, x tile, and x^2 tile represent.

- Demonstration 1 shows how to use algebra tiles to divide $2x^2 + 6x$ by $2x$. First, $2x^2 + 6x$ is modeled. From this model, the two x^2 tiles and one x tile are placed on the product mat transparency. Students are asked to build the rectangle with the remaining tiles on the mat. The length is $2x$ and the width is $x + 3$. The width, $x + 3$, is the quotient of $2x^2 + 6x$ and $2x$.

- Demonstration 2 models the quotient of $x^2 + 5x + 6$ and $x + 2$. Like in Demonstration 1, $x^2 + 5x + 6$ is modeled using algebra tiles. Then the x^2 tile and two of the 1 tiles are placed on the product mat. Next, students are asked to build the rectangle with the remaining tiles on the mat. The length is $x + 2$ and the width is $x + 3$. The width, $x + 3$, is the quotient of $x^2 + 5x + 6$ and $x + 2$.

Provide additional examples showing how to use algebra tiles to model dividing polynomials. Let students discover that algebra tiles cannot be used to divide polynomials with non-zero remainders. The latter situation is addressed in the Algebra Activity on page 667 of the Student Edition. Discuss with students how they can divide without using models.

Answers
Answers appear on the teacher demonstration instructions on pages 195–196.

Algebra Activity Recording Sheet

Dividing Polynomials
(p. 197 of this booklet)

Use With the activity on page 667 in Lesson 12-5 of the Student Edition.

Objective Divide a polynomial by a binomial using algebra tiles.

Materials
algebra tiles*
* = available in Overhead Manipulative Resources

Have students read and study the illustration of $x^2 + 3x + 2$ divided by $x + 1$. Discuss the process as a class. Form groups of two or three students to use algebra tiles to complete the Algebra Activity. Ask students to draw the completed rectangle for each of the Exercises 1–4 and to draw around the dimension that is the quotient. Discuss the quotients. Next, have them work Exercise 5. Students cannot model this division using algebra tiles, because of the existence of a non-zero remainder. Discuss with students how they can divide without using models.

Answers
See Teacher Wraparound Edition p. 667.

Mini-Project

Rational Roundup
(p. 198 of this booklet)

Use With Lesson 12-9.

Objective Solve rational equations. Add, subtract, multiply, and divide rational expressions.

Materials
scissors

Have students work in groups to do this Mini-Project. It deals with solving rational equations. Also, the work involves a review of adding, subtracting, multiplying, and dividing rational expressions. There are twelve exercises to do. Students must simplify their answers. Next, they cut out each rectangle displaying the answer to the exercise. Then students match each rectangle with another one with the same answer. Allow each group to explain how they solved at least one of the exercises. Let them answer any questions about their work. See how many groups discovered the mathematical relationship of the answers.

Answers
A, 1; B, 4; C, 3; D, 2; E, 5; F, 6; G, 4; H, 6; I, 2; J, 1; K, 5; L, 3
Match A, J; B, G; C, L; D, I; E, K; F, H
They are the first six natural numbers.

Using Overhead Manipulatives

(Use with Algebra 1, Lesson 12-5)

Dividing Polynomials by Monomials and by Binomials

Objective Model dividing a polynomial by a monomial and by a binomial.

Materials
- product mat transparency*
- algebra tiles*
- transparency pen*
- two blank transparencies

* = available in Overhead Manipulative Resources

Demonstration 1
Dividing a Binomial by a Monomial

- Point out that algebra tiles used in previous activities are based on the fact that the area of a rectangle is the product of its width and length. Tell students they will use algebra tiles to build rectangles to find quotients.

- Tell students you want to find $(2x^2 + 6x) \div 2x$.

- Ask students how to model $2x^2 + 6x$. **Use 2 x^2 tiles and 6 x tiles.**

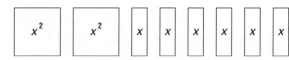

- Display the product mat transparency. Place 2 x^2 tiles at the corner of the product mat. Then place one of the x tiles as shown.

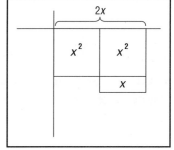

- Ask students how to complete the rectangle on the product mat. **Place 3 x tiles under the first x^2 tile, and 2 x tiles under the second x^2 tile**

- Have students identify the length and width of the rectangle. **length, 2x; width, $x + 3$**

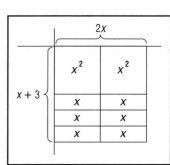

- Ask students which dimension of the rectangle represents the quotient of $2x^2 + 6x$ and $2x$. **the width**

- Have them identify the quotient. **$x + 3$**
  Write $(2x^2 + 6x) \div 2x = x + 3$ on the transparency.

Algebra 1—Chapter 12

Demonstration 2
Dividing a Polynomial by a Binomial

- Tell students you want to find $(x^2 + 5x + 6) \div (x + 2)$.

- Ask students how to model $x^2 + 5x + 6$.
  1 x^2 tile, 5 x tiles, and 6 1 tiles

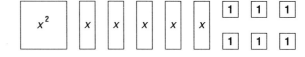

- Display the product mat transparency. Place the x^2 tile at the corner of the product mat. Then place two of the 1 tiles as shown at the right to make a length of $x + 2$.

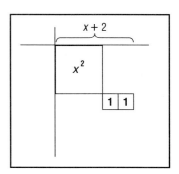

- Have students tell how to complete the rectangle on the product mat. **Place 2 x tiles on the right side of the x^2 tile, 3 x tiles below the x^2 tile, and 4 of the 1 tiles in the right corner to complete the rectangle.**

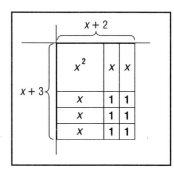

- Ask students to identify the length and width of the rectangle. **length, $x + 2$; width, $x + 3$**

- Have students tell which dimension of the rectangle represents the quotient of $(x^2 + 5x + 6)$ and $(x + 2)$ **the width**

- Ask students to name the quotient. **$x + 3$**
  Write $(x^2 + 5x + 6) \div (x + 2) = (x + 3)$ on the transparency.

Algebra Activity Recording Sheet

(Use with the activity on page 667 in Lesson 12-5 of the Student Edition.)

Dividing Polynomials

Materials: algebra tiles

Model and Analyze
Use algebra tiles to find each quotient.

1. $(x^2 + 3x - 4) \div (x - 1)$

2. $(x^2 - 5x + 6) \div (x - 2)$

3. $(x^2 - 16) \div (x + 4)$

4. $(2x^2 - 4x - 6) \div (x - 3)$

5. Describe what happens when you try to model $(3x^2 - 4x + 3) \div (x + 2)$. What do you think the result means?

Algebra 1—Chapter 12

Mini-Project

(Use with Algebra 1, Lesson 12-9)

Rational Roundup

Work in pairs. Solve the problems. Cut out the rectangles and match each rectangle with another one with the same answer.

A. Simplify. $$\frac{3-c}{c-3} \div \frac{9-3c}{3c-9}$$	**G.** Solve. $$\frac{x-1}{x-2} = \frac{3}{2}$$
B. Solve. $$\frac{2}{5-x} = \frac{2}{x-3}$$	**H.** Solve. $$\frac{3}{2y} - \frac{6}{2y+y^2} = \frac{1}{y+2}$$
C. Simplify. $$\frac{3y+15}{y} \div \frac{y+5}{y}$$	**I.** Simplify. $$\frac{x-5y}{x+y} + \frac{x+7y}{x+y}$$
D. Solve. $$\frac{5n}{12} - \frac{1}{6} = \frac{2}{3}$$	**J.** Simplify. $$\frac{x^2+2x-15}{x^2+4x-5} \cdot \frac{x^2+x-2}{x^2-6-x}$$
E. Simplify. $$\frac{4x^2}{3y} \cdot \frac{135xy}{36x^3}$$	**K.** Simplify. $$\frac{5x-10}{3} \div \frac{2x-4}{6}$$
F. Simplify. $$\frac{3x+6}{5} \div \frac{x+2}{10}$$	**L.** Simplify. $$\frac{12x^2-48}{4x^2-16}$$

Now that you have completed the match, you will see that the final answers have a mathematical relationship. What is it?

Statistics
Teaching Notes and Overview

 ### *Algebra Activity*
Modeling Data
(pp. 200–202 of this booklet)

Use With Lesson 13-3.

Objectives Collect, organize, and display data in a histogram. Use the problem-solving strategy *make a table* to find various ways to make sums for two dice and to display data in a graph.

Materials
for each pair of students,
grid paper
two dice
colored pencils
scissors
tape

This Algebra Activity involves two activities. In the first activity, students roll dice and record the sums in order to have some real-world data to graph. Before beginning this activity, have students guess which sums will be rolled most frequently. Have students work in pairs. Each student can roll a pair of dice 25 times to make the collection of data go more quickly. After the students have finished, you may want to compile the data for the class and graph it to see how the class graph compares to the graphs of each group.

In the second activity, students use a table to record the various ways to make sums from two dice. Each pair needs two-different colored dice. Students can use this information to understand why certain sums occurred more often in the first activity. Point out that the sum 1 + 3 is different from 3 + 1. Using different colored dice will help them to keep track. Students will see that the sum of 7 should occur most frequently and that the sums of 2 and 12 will seldom occur. Interested students may want to design games where various points are awarded for certain sums that are rolled.

Answers

1. See students' graphs.

2. The sums of 2, 3, 11, and 12 occur very seldom. The sums of 6, 7, and 8 occur fairly often.

 ### *Algebra Activity Recording Sheet*
Investigating Percentiles
(p. 203 of this booklet)

Use With Lesson 13-5 as a follow up activity. This corresponds to the activity on pages 743–744 in the Student Edition.

Objective Collect and analyze data dealing with percentiles, and then, make a conjecture, and conduct an investigation.

Materials
grid paper

Ask students to read the information at the top of the recording sheet. Then question the students about the information to check on their understanding. Students should know the meaning and the relationship between a percentile and the cumulative frequency table.

Direct the students' attention to the SAT data in the Collect Data section. Discuss the SAT results displayed in both tables and in the histograms. Ask questions about the data. Let students tell what the data shows.

Divide the class into groups of two or three students. Tell students that there are three sets of exercises to complete, namely, Exercises 1–3, 4–7, and 8. After each set of exercises is completed, the groups will compare and discuss answers. You may need to monitor each group to check on their progress as they work on each set.

Interested students may want to do an investigation of data similar to Exercise 8. Have them share their investigation and results with the class.

Answers
See Teacher Wraparound Edition pp. 743–744.

Algebra Activity

(Use with Algebra 1, Lesson 13-3)

Modeling Data

Materials: two different-colored dice, colored pencils, grid paper, scissors, tape

If you completed the first activity, you made a graph displaying the sums of two dice that you rolled. In the second activity, you will examine the various ways that sums can be rolled for two dice.

Collect the Data

Step 1   Get the two dice. Notice that the only way to get a sum of 2 is roll a 1 and a 1. You can get a sum of 3 in two ways. The red die can be a 1 and the green die can be a 2 and the red die can be a 2 and the green die a 1. Complete the table below by examining the various ways to make each sum.

Sum of Dice	Ways to Make the Sum	Frequency
2	1 + 1	1
3	1 + 2, 2 + 1	2
4	1 + 3, 2 + 2, 3 + 1	3
5		
6		
7		
8		
9		
10		
11		
12		

Step 2   Make a histogram for the data on grid paper. Color the bars.

Teaching Algebra with Manipulatives

Analyze the Data

1. Cut out the graph from Step 2 and tape it in the space below.

2. Describe any patterns in the data from the completed table in Step 1.

3. Write a paragraph below to describe any similarities or differences between the histogram from the first activity and the histogram from this activity.

Algebra Activity

(Use with Algebra 1, Lesson 13-3)

Modeling Data

Materials: two dice, colored pencils, scissors, tape, grid paper

Modeling Data involves two activities. In the first activity, you will perform an experiment, collect and organize the data, and display the data in a graph.

Collect the Data

Step 1   Roll a pair of dice. Find the sum of the numbers that appear face up on the two dice. In the frequency table, make a tally mark in the correct row for that sum. Repeat until you have rolled the pair of dice 50 times.

Step 2   Count the tally marks for each sum and fill in the frequency column.

Step 3   Make a histogram for the data on grid paper. Color in the bars.

Sum of Dice	Tally	Frequency
2		
3		
4		
5		
6		
7		
8		
9		
10		
11		
12		

Analyze the Data

1. Cut out the graph from Step 3 and tape it in the space below.

2. Write a paragraph below to describe the results of your experiment.

NAME _____ DATE _____ PERIOD _____

Algebra Activity Recording Sheet

(Use with the Lesson 13-5 Follow-Up Activity on pages 743–744 in the Student Edition.)

Investigating Percentiles

Materials: grid paper

Analyze the Data

1. Examine the data in the two tables. Explain how the numbers in Column 3 of Table 2 are determined.

2. Describe the similarities and differences between the two histograms.

3. Which histogram do you prefer for displaying these data? Explain your choice.

Make a Conjecture

4. Use the histogram for Table 2. Place percentile labels on the vertical axis. For example, write 100% next to 160 and 0% next to 0. Now label 25%, 50%, and 75%. What numbers of students correspond to 25%, 50%, and 75%?

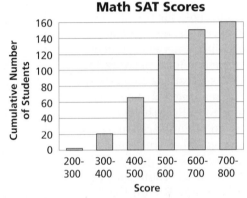

5. Suppose a college is interested in students with scores in the 90th percentile. Using the histogram, move up along the vertical axis to the 90th percentile. Then move right on the horizontal axis to find the score. What is an estimate for the score that represents the 90th percentile?

6. For a more accurate answer, use a proportion to find 90% of the total number of students. (Recall that the total number of students is 160.)

7. If a student is to be in the 90th percentile, in what interval will the score lie?

Extend the Activity

Refer to the data on p. 744. Record your answers on the back of this sheet of paper.

8. Make a cumulative frequency table for the data.

9. Make a cumulative frequency histogram for the data.

10. Find the weight for a baby in the 80th percentile.

Chapter
14

Probability
Teaching Notes and Overview

Algebra Activity Recording Sheet
Finite Graphs
(p. 206 of this booklet)

Use With Lesson 14-1 as a follow-up activity. This corresponds to the activity on page 759 in the Student Edition.

Objective Determine whether or not a network is traceable.

Materials
blank transparency
transparency pen*
* = available in Overhead Manipulative Resources

Form groups of two students for this activity. Before working the exercises, have the groups read about a finite graph, a network, a node, an edge and what it means for a network to be traceable. Ask students questions to check their understanding of the reading. Have each group follow the three steps to Collect the Data. You may want to display on a blank transparency, the graph that represents the streets on Alek's newspaper route. As soon as the groups finish, ask them to tell and show the route they chose for Alek on the transparency. Record the four possible routes by listing the order of the street/avenue used. After listing the routes, have them complete Exercises 1–8. When the work is completed, discuss all of the responses to the exercises.

Answers
See Teacher Wraparound Edition p. 759.

Algebra Activity
Probability and Compound Events
(p. 207 of this booklet)

Use With Lesson 14-3.

Objective Investigate the probability of compound events in which the simple events are joined by the word *and*.

Materials
2 paper bags
2 red counters
2 white counters

Do the **Collect the Data** part of this activity with the whole class. Ask a volunteer to remove a counter from each bag and then to return the counters to their respective bags. Select a volunteer to record the color combination, that is, red/white or white/red or white/white, in the order that each student drew the counters on a transparency, board, or sketchpad. You may want to suggest that they label the bags 1 and 2, and always draw out of bag 1 first, and replace the counter immediately to prevent mixing up the bags. Repeat 99 times. Students at their seats may record the information in the space provided on their worksheet. As a class, complete each exercise and discuss the answers.

Answers

1. Sample answer: about 25%

2. Sample answer: about 25%

3. Sample answer: about 25%

4. Sample answer: about 25%

Algebra Activity
Theoretical and Experimental Probability
(p. 208 of this booklet)

Use With Lesson 14-5.

Objective Compare theoretical probability and experimental probability by performing an experiment in which the outcomes are known.

Materials
paper bag
20 two-inch pieces of paper

In this activity, students perform an experiment in which the outcomes are known. They know how many of each letter is placed in the bag and can easily calculate the theoretical probability. Theoretical probabilities are determined mathematically and describe what should happen. Whereas, experimental probability is determined by using data from tests or experiments.

Provide a paper bag for each group of two students and 20 two-inch pieces of paper. Ask the pairs to follow the steps to **Collect the Data** on the worksheet. Then have them complete Exercises 1–4. As soon as all pairs have finished the activity, collect the data from all groups. Examine the data as a class. Discuss how having a larger set of data affects how close the experimental probability is to the theoretical probability.

Answers

1. See students' work.

2. $P(X) = 20\%$, $P(Y) = 35\%$, $P(Z) = 45\%$

3. See students' work.

4. It should closely resemble the theoretical probability.

Algebra Activity Recording Sheet

Simulations
(p. 209 of this booklet)

Use With the activity on page 783 in Lesson 14-5 of the Student Edition.

Objective Find experimental and theoretical probabilities of rolling a given number on a die.

Materials
die

Students will roll a die 20 times and record the results. They then list the experimental probability of rolling each number. Students then find the theoretical probability of rolling given numbers and compare these results with their experimental probabilities. Finally, they draw conclusions based on the relationship between the number of experiments in a simulation and the experimental probability.

Answers
See Teacher Wraparound Edition p. 783.

Algebra 1—Chapter 14

Algebra Activity Recording Sheet

(Use with the Lesson 14-1 Follow-Up Activity on page 759 in the Student Edition.)

Finite Graphs

Materials: none

Collect the Data
Use the graph at the right.

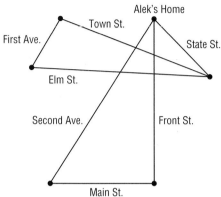

Analyze the Data
1. Is Alek's route traceable? If so, describe his route.

2. Is there more than one traceable route that begins at Alek's house? If so, how many?

3. Suppose it does not matter where Alek starts his route. How many traceable routes are possible now?

Determine whether each graph is traceable. Explain your reasoning.

4.    **5.** 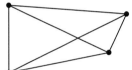   **6.**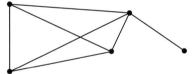

7. The campus for Centerburgh High School has five buildings built around the edge of a circular courtyard. There is a sidewalk between each pair of buildings.

   a. Use the space at the right to draw a graph of the campus.

   b. Is the graph traceable?

   c. Suppose that there is not a sidewalk between the pairs of adjacent buildings. Is it possible to reach all five buildings without walking down any sidewalk more than once?

8. Make a conjecture for a rule to determine whether a graph is traceable.

Algebra Activity

(Use with Algebra 1, Lesson 14-3)

Probability and Compound Events

Materials: 2 paper bags, 2 red counters, 2 white counters

Collect the Data

Step 1   Place a red counter and a white counter in each bag.

Step 2   Without looking, remove one counter from each bag. Record the color combination in the order that you drew the counters. Return the counters to their respective bags.

Step 3   Repeat 99 times. Count and record the number of red/red, white/red, and white/white combinations. Record your results in the space below.

Analyze the Data

1. *P*(red and red)

2. *P*(red and white)

3. *P*(white and red)

4. *P*(white and white)

Algebra Activity

(Use with Algebra 1, Lesson 14-5)

Theoretical and Experimental Probability

Materials: paper bag, 20 two-inch pieces of paper

Collect the Data

Step 1   Mark 4 slips of paper with an X, 7 slips of paper with a Y, and 9 slips of paper with a Z.

Step 2   Put the slips of paper into the bag and mix well.

Step 3   Draw one slip of paper from the bag and record its letter. Use the space below to record your results.

Step 4   Return the slip of paper to the bag and mix well. Repeat Steps 3 and 4 until you have completed 20 trials.

Analyze the Data

1. Calculate the experimental probability of choosing each letter. Express each probability as a percent.

2. Calculate the theoretical probability of choosing each letter.

Make a Conjecture

3. Compare the experimental probability with the theoretical probability. How similar are they?

4. Predict what will happen to the experimental probability as you increase the number of trials.

208   *Teaching Algebra with Manipulatives*

Algebra Activity Recording Sheet

(Use with the activity on page 783 in Lesson 14-5 of the Student Edition.)

Simulations

Materials: die

Analyze the Data

1. Find the theoretical probability of rolling a 2.

2. Find the theoretical probability of rolling a 1 or a 6.

3. Find the theoretical probability of rolling a value less than 4.

4. Compare the experimental and theoretical probabilities. Which pair of probabilities was closer to each other: your individual probabilities or your class's probabilities?

5. Suppose each person rolls the die 50 times. Explain how this would affect the experimental probabilities for the class.

Make a Conjecture

6. What can you conclude about the relationship between the number of experiments in a simulation and the experimental probability?

© Glencoe/McGraw-Hill **209** *Teaching Algebra with Manipulatives*

The Language of Algebra
Teaching Notes and Overview

Algebra Activity Recording Sheet

Distributive Property
(p. 212 of this booklet)

Use With the activity on page 13 in Lesson 1-2 of the Student Edition.

Objective Modeling the distributive property.

Materials
product mat*
algebra tiles*
* = available in Overhead Manipulative Resources

Explain how algebra tiles can be used to model multiplication. Review how to find the area of a rectangle. Go over Steps 1–3 on the Algebra Activity Recording Sheet. Using the tiles, you may want to imitate the step-by-step process on the overhead projector. Allow sufficient time for students to do the exercises. Go over their results. Next, as an extension to the exercises, have students give a new example of a true statement, and another new example of a false statement. Have them demonstrate with their algebra tiles. Discuss the examples.

Answers
See Teacher Wraparound Edition p. 13.

Algebra Activity Recording Sheet

Investigating Polygons and Patterns
(p. 213 of this booklet)

Use With Lesson 1-2 as a follow-up activity. This corresponds to the activity on page 19 of the Student Edition.

Objective Draw polygons and their diagonals to identify patterns among the number of sides, vertices, and diagonals.

Materials
ruler

Students construct six polygons with the number of sides ranging from three to eight. They draw the diagonals for each polygon and record their results in a table. Students then use these polygons and the table to identify and describe patterns that exist among the number of sides, vertices, and diagonals. They also write formulas that express these relationships.

Answers
See Teacher Wraparound Edition p. 19.

Algebra Activity

Solving Equations
(pp. 214–215 of this booklet)

Use With Lesson 1-3.

Objective Solving equations using the properties of equality.

Materials
classroom set of Algebra Activity worksheets
transparency master of Algebra Activity
3-by-5-inch index cards

Prior to class, make the transparency and cut it on the dashed lines. Discuss a strategy for a brother and sister to clean their own rooms. (Each person collects dirty clothes, dirty dishes, and so on.)

Display the transparency to show the "clean your room" strategy for solving equations. Compare combining like terms to collecting laundry or dishes. Solve the simplified equation shown at the bottom of the transparency.

Distribute the Algebra Activity worksheet. Assign pairs of students different equations from the worksheet. (Example: $2x + 3 + 5x = x + 8 + x$) Have them write each term of the equation on a separate index card. ($2x$ 3 $5x = x$ 8 x)

Tell students to simulate cleaning a room by stacking like terms on each side of the equals sign and adding them together.

$2x$	3	x	8
$5x$		x	
$7x$ +	3 =	$2x$ +	8

Record the simplified equation on the worksheet. Then have students solve the simplified equations. For additional practice, ask students to trade their set of cards with others and complete the worksheet.

Answers

1. $9x - 6 = 13x - 8; x = \frac{1}{2}$
2. $44 - 3x = 4 + 5x; x = 5$
3. $5x - 17 = 15 + x; x = 8$
4. $8x + 15 = 47 - 8x; x = 2$
5. $x - 3 = 11x + 4; x = -\frac{7}{10}$
6. $3x + 2 = 4x + 5; x = -3$
7. $6x - 66 = 4 + 8x; x = -35$
8. $x - 17 = 4x - 18; x = \frac{1}{3}$
9. $10x - 14 = -24x + 20; x = 1$
10. $-6x + 12 = 5x - 10; x = 2$
11. $3x - 2 = 26 - 4x; x = 4$
12. $-6 - 18x = -42x - 126; x = -5$

Answers

1. Students are looking for a pattern.
2. Answers may vary. Students may say that the graph of $|x - a| < b$ is the same as the graph of $|x| < b$, but shifted a units to the right.
3. See students' graphs
4. $a, 0; b, 1; c, 2; d, 3$
5. See students' graphs
6. See students' graphs

Mini-Project

Solving Absolute Value Inequalities
(p. 216 of this booklet)

Use With Lesson 1-6.

Objective Solve absolute value inequalities. Let students work in pairs to do Exercises 1 and 2. Have students share and discuss the pattern illustrated in Exercise 1. Ask three of the groups to display their description of the pattern. In Exercise 3 they are asked to use that pattern to graph the absolute value inequality. Review the meaning of midpoint. After finding the midpoint of each graph in Exercise 1, have them describe the pattern in their own words. Now, they should be prepared to graph Exercises 5 and 6. In addition, have them identify the midpoint of each graph too.

Algebra Activity Recording Sheet

(Use with the activity on page 13 in Lesson 1-2 of the Student Edition.)

Distributive Property

Materials: product mat, algebra tiles

Model and Analyze

Tell whether each statement is true or false. Justify your answer with algebra tiles and a drawing.

1. $4(x + 2) = 4x + 2$

2. $3(2x + 4) = 6x + 7$

3. $2(3x + 5) = 6x + 10$

4. $(4x + 1)5 = 4x + 5$

Algebra Activity Recording Sheet

(Use with the Lesson 1-2 Follow-Up Activity on page 19 in the Student Edition.)

Investigating Polygons and Patterns

Materials: ruler

Collect the Data

1. Record your results in the table below.

Figure Name	Sides (n)	Diagonals	Diagonals From One Vertex
triangle	3	0	0
quadrilateral	4	2	1
pentagon	5		
hexagon	6		
heptagon	7		
octagon	8		

Analyze the Data

2. Describe the pattern shown by the number of diagonals in the table above.

3. Complete the last column in the table above.

4. Write an expression in terms of n that relates the number of diagonals from one vertex to the number of sides for each polygon.

5. If a polygon has n sides, how many vertices does it have?

6. How many vertices does one diagonal connect?

Make a Conjecture

7. Write a formula in terms of n for the number of diagonals of a polygon of n sides. (*Hint:* Consider your answers to Exercises 2, 3, and 4.)

8. Draw a polygon on the back of this sheet with 10 sides. Test your formula for the decagon.

9. Explain how your formula relates to the number of vertices of the polygon and the number of diagonals that can be drawn from each vertex. Use the back of this sheet for more space.

Extend the Activity

10. Use the back of this sheet for your drawings.

11. Complete the table at the right.

12. Use any method to find a formula that relates the number of dots, x, to the number of lines, y.

13. Explain why the formula works.

Dots (x)	Connection Lines (y)
3	3
4	
5	
6	
7	
8	

Algebra Activity Transparency Master
(Use with Algebra 2, Lesson 1-3)

Solving Equations

$$2x + 6 + x$$
Brother's Room Before

$$=$$

$$7x - 5x + 8$$
Sister's Room Before

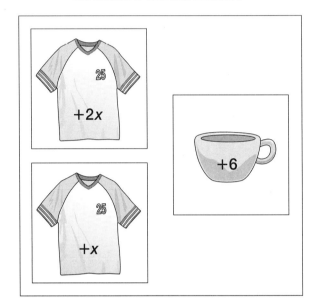

=

Brother's Room After

Sister's Room After

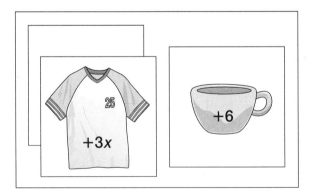

=

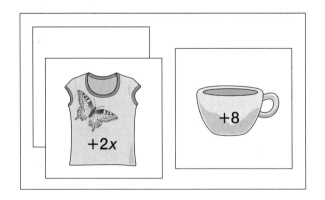

$$
\begin{array}{rcl}
3x + 6 & = & 2x + 8 \\
-2x & & -2x \\
\hline
x + 6 & = & 8 \\
-6 & & -6 \\
\hline
x & = & 2
\end{array}
$$

Teaching Algebra with Manipulatives

NAME _____ DATE _____ PERIOD ____

Algebra Activity

(Use with Algebra 2, Lesson 1-3)

Solving Equations

Simplify each side of the equation. Then solve for x.

1. $4x - 6 + 5x = 13x - 8$

2. $36 - 3x + 8 = 5 + 5x - 1$

3. $x - 8 - 9 + 4x = 15 + x$

4. $5x + 15 + 3x = 72 - 8x - 25$

5. $-3x + 4x - 3 = 8x + 4 + 3x$

6. $4x + 2 - x = 4x + 5$

7. $3x - 66 + 3x = 12 + 8x - 8$

8. $2x - 17 - x = 4x - 22 - 2x + 4 + 2x$

9. $10x - 10 - 4 = 3x - 27x + 20$

10. $-2x + 10 - 4x + 2 = 4x + 3 + x - 13$

11. $3x + 2 - 4 = 30 - 4x - 4$

12. $9 - 18x - 15 = -52x - 126 + 10x$

Mini-Project

(Use with Algebra 2, Lesson 1-6)

Solving Absolute Value Inequalities

Complete the activity below.

1. Look for a pattern. As soon as you recognize one, see if the rest of the exercises fit the pattern.

   a. $|x| < 5$

   b. $|x - 1| < 5$

   c. $|x - 2| < 5$

   d. $|x - 3| < 5$

   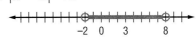

2. Describe the pattern you found. Make up additional examples to test your pattern.

3. Use the pattern to graph $|x - 4| < 5$.

4. What is the midpoint of each segment in Exercise 1?

Graph each inequality and observe the pattern.

5. **a.** $|x| > 6$

   b. $|x - 1| > 6$

   c. $|x - 2| > 6$

   d. $|x - 3| > 6$

6. **a.** $|x| > 3$

   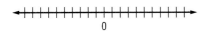

   b. $|x + 1| > 3$

   c. $|x + 2| > 3$

   d. $|x + 3| > 3$

Linear Relations and Functions
Teaching Notes and Overview

Algebra Activity Recording Sheet

Head versus Height
(p. 218 of this booklet)

Use With the activity on page 83 in Lesson 2-5 of the Student Edition.

Objective Find and use prediction equations.

Materials
tape measures

Form groups of two or three students to collect the data for this activity. Have each group measure their height and the circumference of their head. Then have them record the measurements in ordered pairs (height, circumference). Next, ask them to gather the data from the other groups. Using the data, each group makes a scatter plot and completes Exercises 2 through 5. Allow time for students to share and explain their work.

Answers
See Teacher Wraparound Edition p. 83.

Mini-Project

Graphing Absolute Functions
(p. 219 of this booklet)

Use With Lesson 2-6.

Objective Graph absolute value functions.

Have students work in pairs. As soon as each pair has finished tracing the graph of $y = |x|$, you may want to do Exercise 1 with the class. Prior to class, prepare a transparency of the graph of $y = |x|$, and also, have another coordinate grid transparency to show the graph of $y = |x + 1|$. Then model the same procedure as the students. Make the graph for $y = |x + 1|$ on the transparency. Place the graph of $y = |x + 1|$ on the graph of $y = |x|$. Ask the students to compare the two graphs. Display the answer.

Materials
acetate sheet or tracing paper
2 coordinate grid transparency*
* = available in Overhead Manipulative Resources

Answers

1. shift graph of $y = |x|$ up 1 unit
2. shift graph of $y = |x|$ up 2 units
3. shift graph of $y = |x|$ down 1 unit
4. shift graph of $y = |x|$ right 1 unit
5. shift graph of $y = |x|$ right 2 units
6. shift graph of $y = |x|$ right 3 units
7. shift graph of $y = |x|$ left 1 unit
8. shift graph of $y = |x|$ left 2 units
9. shift graph of $y = |x|$ left 3 units
10. shift graph of $y = |x|$ right 1 unit and up 1 unit
11. shift graph of $y = |x|$ right 3 units and up 2 units
12. shift graph of $y = |x|$ left 2 units and down 3 units

Algebra 2—Chapter 2

Algebra Activity Recording Sheet

(Use with the activity on page 83 in Lesson 2-5 of the Student Edition.)

Head versus Height

Materials: tape measure

Analyze the Data

1. Graph the data in a scatter plot.

2. Choose two ordered pairs and write a prediction equation.

3. Explain the meaning of the slope in the prediction equation.

Make a Conjecture

4. Predict the head circumference of a person who is 66 inches tall.

5. Predict the height of an individual whose head circumference is 18 inches.

Mini-Project

(Use with Algebra 2, Lesson 2-6)

Graphing Absolute Value Functions

Trace the graph of $y = |x|$ below on an acetate sheet or on tracing paper. Then place it appropriately on the coordinate plane based on the changes in the equation. Explain how you determine the new position from the original shown.

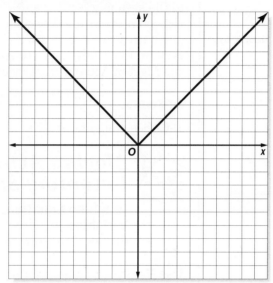

1. $y = |x| + 1$

2. $y = |x| + 2$

3. $y = |x| - 1$

4. $y = |x - 1|$

5. $y = |x - 2|$

6. $y = |x - 3|$

7. $y = |x + 1|$

8. $y = |x + 2|$

9. $y = |x + 3|$

10. $y = |x - 1| + 1$

11. $y = |x - 3| + 2$

12. $y = |x + 2| - 3$

Systems of Equations and Inequalities
Teaching Notes and Overview

Mini-Project
Solving Systems of Linear Equations by Elimination
(p. 222 of this booklet)

Use With Lesson 3-2.

Objective Solve systems of linear equations by elimination.

Materials
scissors
tracing paper

Have students trace and make multiple copies of the models on the Mini-Project page. Ask them to cut the models out. Display a system of linear equations and illustrate how to use the models to find the solution.

Answers

1. $(2, 1)$	**2.** $(0, 4)$	**3.** $(2, 1)$
4. $(4, 2)$	**5.** $(-2, 1)$	**6.** $(-1, 1)$

Algebra Activity
Graphing Systems of Inequalities
(pp. 223–224 of this booklet)

Use With Lesson 3-3.

Objective Graph systems of inequalities.

Materials
classroom set of Algebra Activity worksheets
transparency master of Algebra Activity
blue and yellow acetate sheets

Review graphing linear equations and inequalities. Remind students that solid lines are used for inequalities $\geq$ or $\leq$ and dashed lines are used for inequalities involving $>$ or $<$. Now explain the process of graphing a system of inequalities. Graph the inequality $y > x + 2$. Ask students if the following points satisfy the inequality: $(1, 3)$, $(0, 0)$, $(-2, 4)$. Name several points above the dashed line and ask the same question. Have them describe in their own words the set of points that are in the solution set. Place the blue acetate rectangle on the

graph to illustrate the area to be shaded. Ask students if all the points in the blue area satisfy the inequality. Use the same procedure with $y \leq 3x$. Point out the need for the solid line. Place the yellow acetate rectangle in the region below the line. Tell students that the solution to the system $y > x + 2$ and $y < 3x$ is the green region on the graph. Try some points in the green area to check to see if they satisfy the system. In groups, have students complete the Algebra Activity worksheet.

Answers

1–6. See students' graphs.

Algebra Activity Recording Sheet
Graphing Equations in Three Variables
(p. 225 of this booklet)

Use With Lesson 3-5 as a preview activity. This corresponds to the activity on pages 136–137 in the Student Edition.

Objective Graph equations in three variables.

Materials
isometric dot paper (p. 19 of this booklet)
prepare an isometric dot transparency
transparency pen*
* = available in Overhead Manipulative Resources

Be sure students understand that there are three planes in three-dimensional space, namely, xy-plane, xz-plane and the yz-plane. These planes intersect at right angles and divide space into eight regions called **octants**. Give students practice in plotting points in space on isometric dot paper. You can show these points in space on the isometric dot transparency. Some students may need help visualizing three-dimensions on a piece of isometric dot paper. Go over Examples 1 and 2. Have students work these examples at their seats as you do the examples on the overhead projector. In the Model and Analyze section, do the first exercise from each set of Exercises 1 through 12 along with the students. Now form groups of two or three students to work the remaining exercises.

Answers
See Teacher Wraparound Edition pp. 136–137.

 ## *Algebra Activity*

Equations of Planes
(pp. 226–227 of this booklet)

Use With Lesson 3-5.

Objectives Determine the octant in which a point in space is located and graph it.

Graph linear equations in space, and determine the intercepts and traces.

Materials
classroom set of Algebra Activity worksheets
transparency master of Algebra Activity
Tinkertoys® or similar construction toys (6 sticks, 1 circle per group)
string (about 2 feet per group)

Prior to the activity, assemble a set of Tinkertoys® to simulate x-, y-, and z-axes. Calibrate the sticks using 1- or 2-cm intervals. Cut the transparency on the dashed line. Pass out the Algebra Activity worksheet.

Form student groups. Ask the groups to assemble their Tinkertoys® to simulate x-, y-, and z-axes. Show the students your model. Have the students use their Tinkertoy® model to help them answer Exercise 1 on the worksheet.

Next, display the transparency and graph $(3, -2, 6)$ (Figure 1). Then graph $(-2, -5, 4)$ (Figure 2). Then complete Exercise 2 on the worksheet.

Discuss finding the x-, y-, and z-intercepts of the equation $x + 2y + z = 4$. Wrap the string around the sticks on the model, where $x = 4$, $y = 2$, and $z = 4$, connecting the trace in each coordinate plane. Repeat the procedure for $-5x + 15y + 6z = 30$.

Now display the transparency and show the diagram for the above equations, using Figures 3 and 4. Complete the worksheet as a whole group or individual activity.

Answers

1. 1; 5; none

2. See students' graphs.

3a. See students' graphs; $(3, 0, 0)$, $(0, 3, 0)$, $(0, 0, 3)$; $x + y = 3$, $x + z = 3$, $y + z = 3$

3b. See students' graphs; $(3, 0, 0)$, $(0, 6, 0)$, $(0, 0, -2)$; $2x + y = 6$, $2x - 3z = 6$, $y - 3z = 6$

3c. See students' graph; $(-5, 0, 0)$, $(0, 3, 0)$, $(0, 0, -15)$; $-3x + 5y = 15$, $-3x - z = 15$, $5y - z = 15$

3d. See students' graphs; $(4, 0, 0)$, $(0, 3, 0)$, none; $3x = 12$, $4y = 12$, $3x + 4y = 12$

Algebra 2—Chapter 3

Mini-Project

(Use with Algebra 2, Lesson 3-2)

Solving Systems of Linear Equations by Elimination

Trace and make multiple copies of each model below.

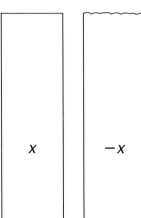

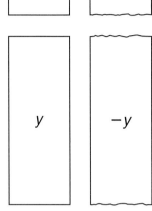

Use the models to demonstrate solving systems of linear equations by elimination.

1. $x + y = 3$
    $x - y = 1$

2. $2x + y = 4$
    $-x + y = 4$

3. $2x + 3y = 7$
    $3x - y = 5$

4. $x + 2y = 8$
    $2x - 3y = 2$

5. $-3x - 2y = 4$
    $5x + 3y = -7$

6. $6x + 3y = -3$
    $-4x - 3y = 1$

Algebra Activity Transparency Master

(Use with Algebra 2, Lesson 3-3)

Graphing Systems of Inequalities

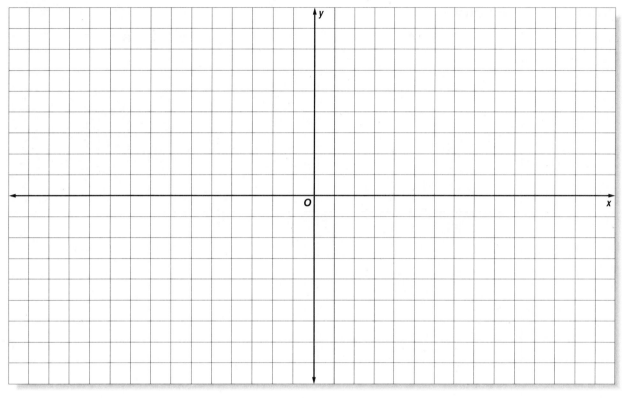

Teaching Algebra with Manipulatives

Algebra Activity
(Use with Algebra 2, Lesson 3-3)

Graphing Systems of Inequalities

Graph each inequality.

1. $x > 2$ **2.** $y < x - 1$ **3.** $2x + y \geq 6$

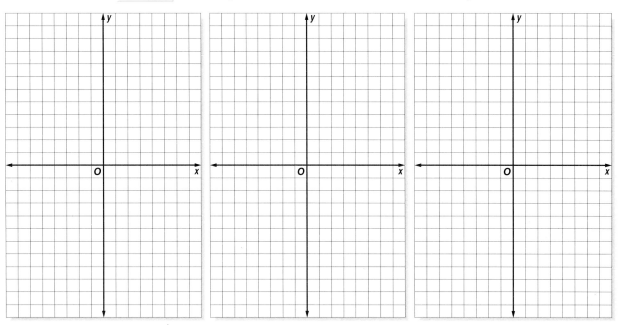

Solve each system of inequalities by graphing.

4. $y > 4$
   $x \leq -1$
                5. $y \geq x + 4$
                     $y < 2x - 2$
                                  6. $x - y > 1$
                                         $x + y > 1$

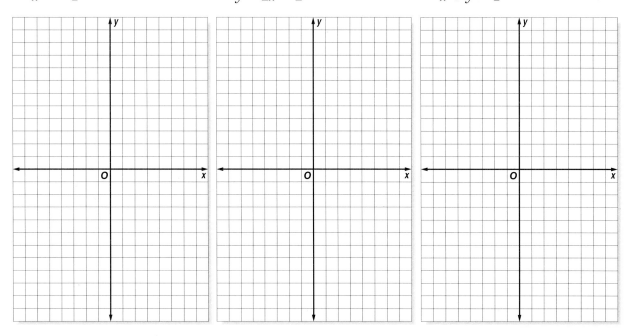

Algebra Activity Recording Sheet

(Use with the Lesson 3-5 Preview Activity on pages 136–137 in the Student Edition.)

Graphing Equations in Three Variables

Materials: isometric dot paper

Model and Analyze

Use a piece of isometric dot paper to graph each ordered triple on
a three-dimensional coordinate system. Name the octant in which
each point lies.

1. $(5, 3, 6)$ _____

2. $(-2, 4, 3)$ _____

3. $(1, -5, 7)$ _____

Use a piece of isometric dot paper to graph each equation. Name
the coordinates for the x-, y-, and z-intercepts.

4. $3x + 6y + z = 6$

5. $2x - 5y + 4z = 20$

6. $x + 3y - 6z = 3$

7. $-3x + 5y + 10z = 15$

8. $6x + 9z = 18$

9. $4x - 6y = 24$

Write an equation of the plane given its x-, y-, and z-intercepts,
respectively.

10. $8, -3, 6$

11. $10, 4, -5$

12. $\frac{1}{2}, 4, -12$

13. Describe the values of $x, y,$ and z as either positive or negative for each
octant.

14. a.   **b.**   **c.**

d. Describe and compare the graphs in parts **a**, **b**, and **c**.

e. Make a conjecture about the graph of $x > -3$ in one, two, and three
dimensions.

Algebra Activity Transparency Master
(Use with Algebra 2, Lesson 3-5)

Equations of Planes

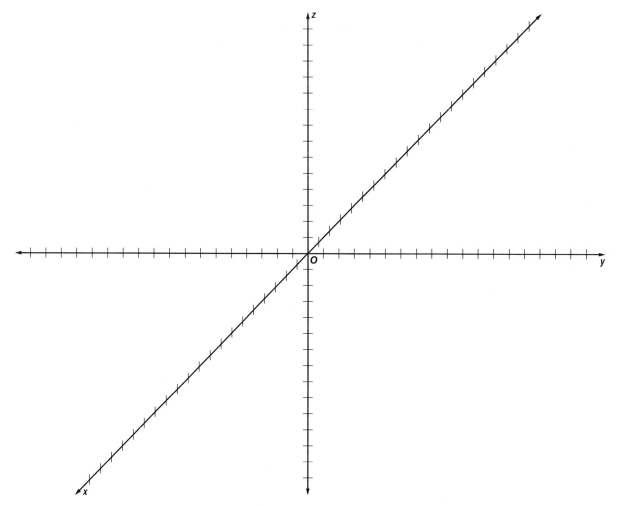

Figure 1	Figure 2	Figure 3

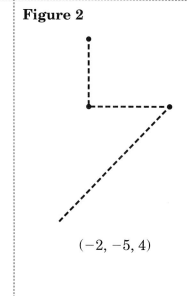

$(3, -2, 6)$

$(-2, -5, 4)$

Figure 3

$x + 2y + z = 4$

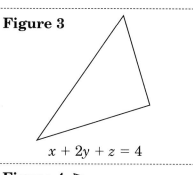

Figure 4

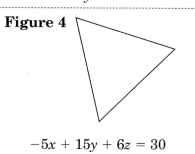

$-5x + 15y + 6z = 30$

Teaching Algebra with Manipulatives

Algebra Activity

(Use with Algebra 2, Lesson 3-5)

Equations of Planes

1. In which octant does each point lie?

(2, 8, 6) _____   (−3, 4, 5) _____   (0, 0, 4) _____

2. Graph the following points.

a. (6, 2, 1)

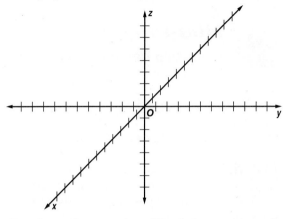

b. (−1, 4, 6)

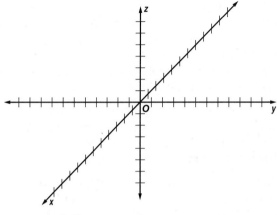

3. Graph each equation. Find the *x*-, *y*-, and *z*-intercepts and the traces in the coordinate planes.

a. $x + y + z = 3$

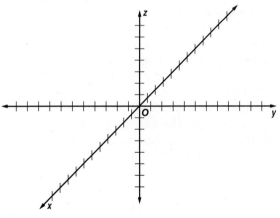

b. $2x + y - 3z = 6$

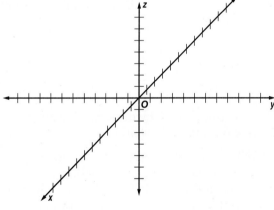

c. $-3x + 5y - z = 15$

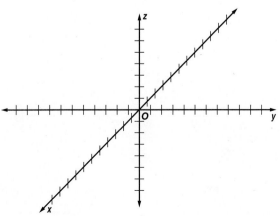

d. $3x + 4y = 12$

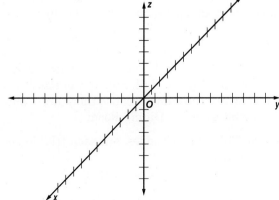

Teaching Algebra with Manipulatives

Matrices
Teaching Notes and Overview

Algebra Activity

Matrices
(pp. 229–230 of this booklet)

Use With Lesson 4-1.

Objective Write and interpret a matrix representation of a finite graph.

Materials
classroom set of Algebra Activity worksheets
transparency master of Algebra Activity

Display the finite graph portion of the transparency on the overhead projector. The dots (vertices) represent the rest stops and the lines (edges) represent the trails.

Define a path as a route from stop to stop not passing through any other stop. Find the total number of paths for each element in the transparency chart. (Note: A path from Cook's Corner to Cook's Corner may be clockwise or counter-clockwise.)

Write the chart in matrix form (omit names of rows and columns).

$$\begin{vmatrix} 2 & 1 & 0 & 1 \\ 1 & 0 & 2 & 1 \\ 0 & 2 & 2 & 1 \\ 1 & 1 & 1 & 0 \end{vmatrix}$$

Reverse the process by drawing a graph of Matrix A on the transparency.

Distribute the Algebra Activity worksheet. Ask students to assist you in completing the chart and writing the matrix for it. Work a couple of rows in the chart and show those rows in the matrix. Form groups of three students to complete the worksheet. As soon as the groups have finished, discuss and share the answers.

Answers

1. Sum of Row 2 = 4. There are 4 paths leading from the Dining Hall. Sum of Column 2 = 4. They are the same because there are 4 paths to and from the Dining Room.

2. 20. There are 10 edges, but each trial leads two ways.

3. $\begin{vmatrix} 0 & 2 & 1 & 0 \\ 2 & 0 & 2 & 1 \\ 1 & 2 & 2 & 0 \\ 0 & 1 & 0 & 0 \end{vmatrix}$ **4.** $\begin{vmatrix} 2 & 1 & 1 & 1 \\ 1 & 0 & 1 & 0 \\ 1 & 1 & 0 & 2 \\ 1 & 0 & 2 & 0 \end{vmatrix}$

5. See students' graphs

6. See students' graphs

Mini-Project

Evaluating Determinants
(p. 231 of this booklet)

Use With Lesson 4-3.

Objective Evaluate determinants.

Materials
for each group of students, two sets of two different colored 4″ by 6″ index cards and scissors

This activity develops the process of evaluating 3×3 determinants. Have students repeat this same process by cutting another set of strips and writing different numbers on them. Ask them to show their work for evaluating the determinant. Let groups exchange their cutouts with another group and evaluate that determinant. Provide additional 3×3 determinants for students to evaluate without using the cutouts. Ask them to find out what happens when the entries in one row of a 3×3 are 0. Encourage them to investigate other properties of determinants.

Algebra Activity

(Use with Algebra 2, Lesson 4-1)

Matrices

Complete the chart. Then write a matrix for the graph at the right. (Remember there is one and only one stop on each path.)

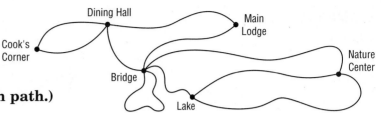

PATHS TO / FROM	Cook's Corner	Dining Hall	Main Lodge	Bridge	Lake	Nature Center
Cook's Corner						
Dining Hall						
Main Lodge						
Bridge						
Lake						
Nature Center						

Matrix

Using the matrix above, complete the following.

1. Add the elements in the second row. What does this number represent in the graph? How does your number compare to the sum of the second column?

_____

2. Add the elements in each row. Find the total of these sums. Is this total related to the number of edges in the graph? If so, how?

_____

Write the matrices corresponding to the graphs.

3.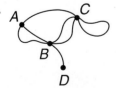

4.

Draw the graphs corresponding to the matrices.

5. $\begin{vmatrix} 2 & 1 & 1 & 0 \\ 1 & 0 & 0 & 1 \\ 1 & 0 & 0 & 0 \\ 0 & 1 & 0 & 2 \end{vmatrix}$

6. $\begin{vmatrix} 2 & 1 & 1 & 1 \\ 1 & 0 & 0 & 1 \\ 1 & 0 & 2 & 0 \\ 1 & 1 & 0 & 2 \end{vmatrix}$

Algebra Activity Transparency Master

(Use with Algebra 2, Lesson 4-1)

Matrices

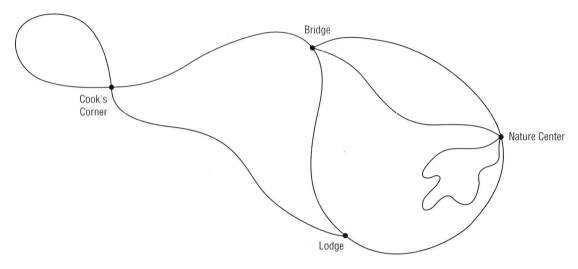

PATHS	TO Cook's Corner	Bridge	Nature Center	Lodge
Cook's Corner	2	1	0	1
Bridge				
Nature Center				
Lodge				

$$\begin{vmatrix} 2 & 1 & 0 & 1 \end{vmatrix}$$

Matrix A

TO

$$\begin{matrix} & A\ B\ C\ D & \\ \text{FROM} \begin{vmatrix} 2 & 2 & 1 & 1 \\ 2 & 2 & 0 & 1 \\ 1 & 0 & 2 & 0 \\ 1 & 1 & 0 & 0 \end{vmatrix} & \begin{matrix} A \\ B \\ C \\ D \end{matrix} \end{matrix}$$

Mini-Project

(Use with Algebra 2, Lesson 4-3)

Evaluating Determinants

Complete the activity below.

Take two different colored 4″ × 6″ index cards and cut each into 6 strips.

Choose any three integers for each strip of one color and randomly write them in a column. Make a matching set of strips of the other color.

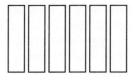

Draw 3 strips at random from one set. Arrange the strips in a 3 × 3 determinant as shown below. Choose 2 columns from the other set that match columns 1 and 2 and place to the right of the determinant. Evaluate each determinant.

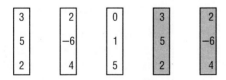

Now find the product of the elements in each diagonal. Add the products of the diagonals that extend from upper left to lower right. Then subtract the products of the other diagonals. The result is the value of the determinant.

$$= (3)(-6)(5) + (2)(1)(2) + (0)(5)(4) - (2)(-6)(0) - (4)(1)(3) - (5)(5)(2)$$
$$= -90 + 4 + 0 - 0 - 12 - 50$$
$$= -148$$

The value of the determinant is −148.

Algebra Activity Recording Sheet

Multiplying Binomials
(p. 234 of this booklet)

Use With the activity on page 230 in Lesson 5 2 of the Student Edition.

Objective Multiply binomials.

Materials
algebra tiles*
* = available in Overhead Manipulative Resources

Give each group of two students a set of algebra tiles and a copy of the Algebra Recording Sheet. Allow students about five minutes to read the Sheet. Once they have completed the reading, ask students questions about the reading. Make sure they understand the directions.

If time permits, assign two more binomials to multiply such as $(x + 3)$ and $(x + 4)$. Let them predict the product before using the tiles for the modeling. Have students explain their prediction.

Answers
See Teacher Wraparound Edition p. 230.

Algebra Activity Recording Sheet

Factoring Trinomials
(p. 235 of this booklet)

Use With the activity on page 240 in Lesson 5-4 of the Student Edition.

Objective Factor trinomials.

Materials
algebra tiles*
* = available in Overhead Manipulative Resources

Have students work in pairs to complete the Algebra Activity Recording Sheet. Provide a set of tiles for each pair. Go over the directions and the drawings under the Model and Analyze heading. Ask questions. Be sure they see the translation of the information obtained from the modeling to

the line-by-line algebraic procedure. Students may benefit from a review of what is meant by the Distributive Property, the greatest common factor, coefficient, and constant term. Go over the responses to the exercises with the class.

If there is time, let students factor another trinomial. Require the pairs of students to make a conjecture about how to factor the trinomial. Bring the pairs together and discuss the conjectures.

Answers
See Teacher Wraparound Edition p. 240.

Algebra Activity

Finding Radical Roots of Polynomials
(pp. 236–237 of this booklet)

Use With Lesson 5-5.

Objective Find radical roots of polynomials.

Materials
classroom set of Algebra Activity worksheets
transparency master of Algebra Activity
25 one-inch square algebra tiles and 4 two-inch square algebra tiles per group

Prior to the class, have a set of tiles ready for each group. Ask each group to complete Exercise 1 on the worksheet. Go over the answers.

Next, display the transparency showing only Figures 1–4. Point out what the figures show. Now uncover Figures 5–7. Discuss the area of each figure in its factored form and examine the square roots. Encourage students to identify the area as perfect squares and the sides as square roots of the area. Use the bottom of the transparency to discuss factoring whole numbers into prime factors and grouping pairs of like factors. Then find the square roots. Emphasize the importance of showing the step-by-step process and being able to explain it. Students may complete the rest of the worksheet in their groups. Call on each group to give their answer to at least one of the exercises. If an explanation is needed, have the students from the group give it. Encourage students to explain their work.

Answers

1. 4, 2; 9, 3; 16, 4; 25, 5

2. See students' models.

3. $x + 2$, $(x + 2)^2$, $(x + 2)(x + 2)$;
   $2x + x$, $(2x + x)^2$, $(2x + x)(2x + x)$;
   $3xy + xy$, $(3xy + xy)^2$, $(3xy + xy)(3xy + xy)$;
   $b + 3$, $(b + 3)^2$, $(b + 3)(b + 3)$

4. 10

5. 9

6. 0.2

7. $\dfrac{3}{11}$

8. $2|x|$

9. $2x^2 \sqrt{6}$

10. $4x^2y^2 \sqrt{14y}$

11. $27x^3y^3 \sqrt{y}$

Algebra Activity Recording Sheet

Adding Radicals
(p. 238 of this booklet)

Use With the activity on page 252 in Lesson 5-6 of the Student Edition.

Objective Use dot paper to add radicals.

Materials
isometric dot paper

Students will use the Pythagorean Theorem to construct a right triangle with hypotenuse of length $\sqrt{2}$ units on dot paper. They will extend the hypotenuse to twice its length and use the models to add the radicals. Students will also model other irrational numbers using the same method.

Answers
See Teacher Wraparound Edition p. 252.

Mini-Project

nth Roots of Negative Numbers
(p. 239 of this booklet)

Use With Lesson 5-9.

Objective Find nth roots of negative numbers.

Have students work in groups of two or three to complete the Exercises 1 through 9. Require students to do and show their work for Exercises 1, 5, and 8. Remind students that when graphing in the complex plane, ordered pairs are in the form (real, imaginary). As soon as students have completed Exercises 1–4, Exercises 5–7, and Exercise 8, you may want to stop and go over their answers and answer any questions they may have. Some students may be interested in investigating, solving, and graphing other similar equations. Encourage them to pursue these interests and to share their findings with the class.

Answers

1–3. See students' work.

4. square

5–6. See students' work.

7. triangle

8. See students' work.

9. regular hexagon

Algebra Activity Recording Sheet

Adding Complex Numbers
(p. 240 of this booklet)

Use With the activity on page 272 in Lesson 5-9 of the Student Edition.

Objective Add complex numbers by modeling them on a coordinate plane.

Materials
grid paper
straightedge

Students will graph the first complex number from an addition equation on a coordinate grid. They will then move accordingly on the grid to add the next complex number. The new point represents the complex number that is the solution to the equation. Using the coordinate grid, students will also model the difference and absolute value of other complex numbers.

Answers
See Teacher Wraparound Edition p. 272.

Algebra Activity Recording Sheet

(Use with the activity on page 230 in Lesson 5-2 of the Student Edition.)

Multiplying Binomials

Materials: algebra tiles

Use algebra tiles to find the product of $x + 5$ and $x + 2$.

1. Draw a 90° angle.

2. Use an x-tile and a 1-tile to mark off a length equal to $x + 5$ along the top.

3. Use the tiles to mark off a length equal to $x + 2$ along the side.

4. Draw lines to show the grid formed by these measures.

5. Fill in the lines with the appropriate tiles to show the area product. The model shows the polynomial $x^2 + 7x + 10$.

The area of the rectangle is the product of its length and width. Substituting for the length, width, and area with the corresponding polynomials, we find that $(x + 5)(x + 2) = x^2 + 7x + 10$.

Algebra Activity Recording Sheet

(Use with the activity on page 230 in Lesson 5-2 of the Student Edition.)

Factoring Trinomials

Materials: algebra tiles

Make a Conjecture
Study the factorization of $2x^2 + 7x + 3$.

1. What are the coefficients of the two x-terms in $(2x^2 + x) + (6x + 3)$? Find their sum and their product.

2. Compare the sum you found in Exercise 1 to the coefficient of the x term in $2x^2 + 7x + 3$.

3. Find the product of the coefficient of the x^2 term and the constant term in $2x^2 + 7x + 3$. How does it compare to the product you found in Exercise 1?

4. Make a conjecture about how to factor $3x^2 + 7x + 2$.

Algebra Activity Transparency Master

(Use with Algebra 2, Lesson 5-5)

Radical Roots of Polynomials

Figure 1

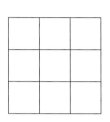

Figure 2

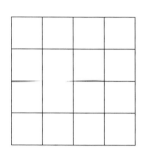

Figure 3

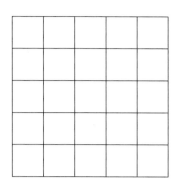

Figure 4

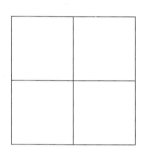

Figure 5

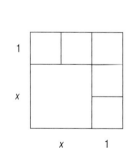

Figure 6

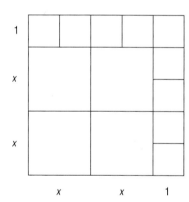

Figure 7

$$\sqrt{100} = \sqrt{(2 \cdot 2) \cdot (5 \cdot 5)} = 2 \cdot 5 = 10$$

$$\sqrt{6x^2y} = \sqrt{2 \cdot 3 \cdot (x \cdot x) \cdot y} = x\sqrt{2 \cdot 3 \cdot y} = x\sqrt{6y}$$

Teaching Algebra with Manipulatives

Algebra Activity

(Use with Algebra 2, Lesson 5-5)

Radical Roots of Polynomials

1. Using one-inch ceramic tiles, make a square with 4, 9, 16, and 25 tiles. Complete the chart below based on your models.

Number of tiles used in model	4	9	16	25
Draw the model.				
Area of the square				
Length of a side				

2. Make a square using four 2-inch tiles and five 1-inch tiles. Draw a picture of the model.

Make a square using four 2-inch tiles and nine 1-inch tiles. Draw a picture of the model.

3. Complete the following chart for the given measures of large and small tiles squares.

Large Square Sides	Small Square Sides	Model Side	Model Area	Prime Factors of Area
x by x	1 by 1	$x + 1$	$(x + 1)^2$	$(x + 1)(x + 1)$
x by x	2 by 2			
$2x$ by $2x$	x by x			
$3xy$ by $3xy$	xy by xy			
b^2 by b^2	3 by 3			

Find each square root.

4. $\sqrt{100}$ _____

5. $\sqrt{81}$ _____

6. $\sqrt{0.04}$ _____

7. $\sqrt{\dfrac{9}{121}}$ _____

8. $\sqrt{4x^2}$ _____

9. $\sqrt{24x^4}$ _____

10. $\sqrt{224x^4y^5}$ _____

11. $\sqrt{729x^6y^7}$ _____

Algebra Activity Recording Sheet

(Use with the activity on page 252 in Lesson 5-6 of the Student Edition.)

Adding Radicals

Materials: isometric dot paper

Make a Conjecture

1. Is $\sqrt{2} + \sqrt{2} = \sqrt{2 + 2}$ or 2? Justify your answer using the geometric models.

2. Use this method to model other irrational numbers. Do these models support your conjecture?

 **Mini-Project**

(Use with Algebra 2, Lesson 5-9)

nth Roots of Negative Numbers

Work in groups of two or three to complete Exercises 1 through 9.

1. Use multiplication to show that $z = 1 + i$, $z = -1 + i$, $z = -1 - i$, and $z = 1 - i$ are the solutions of $z^4 = -4$.

2. Graph the solutions of $z^4 = -4$ on the complex plane.

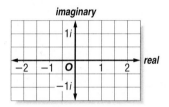

3. Connect the points you graphed for Exercise 2 in the order listed in Exercise 1.

4. What kind of figure did you draw in Exercise 3?

5. Show that $z = \dfrac{1}{2} + \dfrac{\sqrt{3}}{2}i$, $z = \dfrac{1}{2} - \dfrac{\sqrt{3}}{2}i$, and $z = -1$ are the solutions of $z^3 = -1$.

6. Graph the solutions of $z^3 = -1$ on the complex plane.

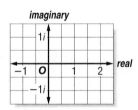

7. Connect the points you graphed for Exercise 6. What kind of figure did you draw?

8. Let $z = \dfrac{1}{2} + \dfrac{\sqrt{3}}{2}i$. Find $z^2, z^3, z^4, z^5,$ and z^6.

9. Graph all six points on the complex plane. If you connect these points in order, what kind of figure is formed?

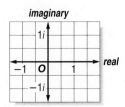

Algebra Activity Recording Sheet

(Use with the activity on page 272 in Lesson 5-9 of the Student Edition.)

Adding Complex Numbers

Materials: grid paper, straightedge

Model and Analyze

1. Model $(-3 + 2i) + (4 - i)$ on a coordinate plane.

2. Describe how you could model the difference $(-3 + 2i) - (4 - i)$ on a coordinate plane.

3. The **absolute value** of a complex number is the distance from the origin to the point representing that complex number in a coordinate plane. Refer to the graph. Find the absolute value of $2 + 5i$.

4. Find an expression for the absolute value of $a + bi$.

6 Quadratic Functions and Inequalities
Teaching Notes and Overview

Mini-Project
Parabolas
(p. 243 of this booklet)

Use With Lesson 6-1.

Objective Write equations for parabolas.

Materials
clear acetate sheet for each group

Have students work in small groups to complete this Mini-Project. Give each group a clear acetate sheet. This sheet will be used to trace the parabola on the worksheet. Using $\frac{1}{4}$-inch grid paper, place the acetate on a coordinate plane with the vertex at the given point. Then have students align the axis with a vertical line of the grid paper. Next, they list five points that the graph contains, and write the equation for the graph. This activity shows students that parabolas with the same shape will have different equations depending on the vertex. Allow students to share and discuss their answers for Exercises 3 and 4.

Some students may become interested in investigating parabolas that face downward. These students may use the same parabola that they traced on acetate paper. Encourage them to write about their findings and share their work with the other students by making a presentation.

Answers

1. See students' trace of graph.

2a. $(-2, 9), (-1, 4), (0, 1), (2, 1), (3, 4), (4, 9)$;
$(x - 1)^2$

2b. $(-1, 9), (0, 4), (1, 1), (3, 1), (4, 4), (5, 9)$;
$(x - 2)^2$

2c. $(0, 9), (1, 4), (2, 1), (4, 1), (5, 4), (6, 9)$; $(x - 3)^2$

2d. $(-4, 9), (-3, 4), (-2, 1), (0, 1), (1, 4), (2, 9)$;
$(x + 1)^2$

2e. $(-3, 11), (-2, 6), (-1, 3), (1, 3), (2, 6), (3, 11)$;
$x^2 + 2$

2f. $(-3, 5), (-2, 0), (-1, -3), (1, -3), (2, 0), (3, 5)$; $x^2 - 4$

2g. $(0, 10), (1, 5), (2, 2), (4, 2), (5, 5), (6, 10)$;
$(x - 3)^2 + 1$

2h. $(-2, 7), (-1, 2), (0, -1), (2, -1), (3, 2), (4, 7)$;
$(x - 1)^2 - 2$

3. $y = (x - h)^2 + k$

4. $y = (x - 2)^2 + 3$

Algebra Activity Recording Sheet
Completing the Square
(p. 244 of this booklet)

Use With the activity on page 308 in Lesson 6-4 of the Student Edition.

Objective Solve quadratic equations by completing the square.

Materials
algebra tiles*
equation mats*
* = available in Overhead Manipulative Resources

You may need to review how to represent a quadratic equation with tiles on the equation mat. Have students follow along as you go over using the mat to complete the square for a quadratic equation. Ask students to work in pairs to complete the square for Exercises 1 through 4.

Answers
See Teacher Wraparound Edition p. 308.

Algebra Activity
Completing the Square
(pp. 245–246 of this booklet)

Use With Lesson 6-4.

Objective Solve quadratic equations by completing the square.

Materials
algebra tiles*
classroom set of Algebra Activity worksheets
transparency master of Algebra Activity
grid paper*
* = available in Overhead Manipulative Resources

Prior to class, cut the transparency master on the dashed line. Cut out each model on the bottom half.

Discuss the definition of a perfect square. Ask students to draw their own representation of a number squared and share the results. Display the transparency master that matches this activity. Use the squares in the top row to discuss how the square of an expression can be represented geometrically.

In groups, have students cut figures from grid paper like the transparency models. Using the models, create a representation for $x^2 + 6x$. Then ask students to determine the number of unit squares needed to make their figures a square. Next, discuss completing the square using Figure A of the transparency. Solve the equation on the transparency with the students. Show students how to check the solution. On the Algebra Activity worksheet, work through Exercises 1 through 6 with the students. Have students solve Exercises 7 through 10 in their groups. As soon as the groups have finished finding the solutions, discuss the solutions.

Answers

1. See students' diagrams; 16

2. See students' diagrams; 1

3. See students' diagrams; 4

4. See students' diagrams; 36

5. $\{-8, 6\}$ 6. $\{-8, 2\}$

7. $\{-5, -3\}$ 8. $\{3, 4\}$

9. $\{-13, 1\}$ 10. $\{3, -13\}$

Algebra Activity

Quadratic Functions
(pp. 247–248 of this booklet)

Use With Lesson 6-6.

Objective Graph families of quadratic functions.

Materials
classroom set of Algebra Activity worksheets
transparency master of Algebra Activity

As part of the preparation for class, cut the transparency master of the Algebra Activity. Display the transparency grid with Figure A overlapping to show $f(x) = x^2$. Then use Figure B to show $f(x) = x^2 + 3$.

Compare the graphs to discover that adding 3 causes a slide transformation. Question students to predict the graph of $f(x) = x^2 - 2$. Then graph it with Figure B. In the same manner as you discussed Figures A and B, compare $f(x) = x^2$ with $f(x) = -x^2$ and talk about the flip transformation.

Next, compare the graph of $f(x) = 2x^2$ (use Figure C) with $f(x) = 2x^2 + 3$ (use Figure D).

Show the four different graphs below on the same grid. Discuss how the coefficients affect the openness of the graph of the parabola.

Fig. A $f(x) = x^2$ Fig. B $f(x) = 2x^2$

Fig. C $f(x) = \frac{1}{2}x^2$ Fig. D $f(x) = \frac{1}{8}x^2$

Be sure students understand what is meant by the axis of symmetry. Using the graphs on the transparency, illustrate the axis of symmetry and discuss the equation for it. Write the equation on each graph. In groups, have students complete the worksheet. Allow time to discuss the answers to the exercises.

Answers

1–6. See students' graphs.

7. The parabolas have the same shape.

8. Their vertex is the origin.

9. 4 and 5 open up, 6 opens down.

10a. $(0, 0)$, $y = 0$ **10b.** $(0, 5)$, $y = 0$ **10c.** $(0, -4)$, $y = 0$ **10d.** $(0, 0)$, $y = 0$ **10e.** $(0, 0)$, $y = 0$ **10f.** $(0, 0)$, $y = 0$

11. $f(x) = (x - 0)^2 + 0$; $f(x) = (x - 0)^2 + 5$; $f(x) = (x - 0)^2 - 4$; $f(x) = 4(x - 0)^2 + 0$; $f(x) = \frac{1}{4}(x - 0)^2 + 0$; $f(x) = -6(x - 0)^2 + 0$;

The vertex is (h, k).
The axis of symmetry is $y = h$.

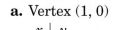

Mini-Project

(Use with Algebra 2, Lesson 6-1)

Parabolas

Work in small groups to complete the activity.

1. Trace the parabola given to the right onto a piece of clear acetate.

2. Using $\frac{1}{4}$-inch grid paper, place the acetate on a coordinate plane with the vertex at the given point. Align the axis with a vertical line of the grid paper. List five points that the graph contains. Complete the equation for the graph.

Axis

Vertex

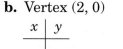

a. Vertex $(1, 0)$

x	y

$y =$

b. Vertex $(2, 0)$

x	y

$y =$

c. Vertex $(3, 0)$

x	y

$y =$

d. Vertex $(-1, 0)$

x	y

$y =$

e. Vertex $(0, 2)$

x	y

$y =$

f. Vertex $(0, -4)$

x	y

$y =$

g. Vertex $(3, 1)$

x	y

$y =$

h. Vertex $(1, -2)$

x	y

$y =$

3. Based on the results above, what equation can you write for a parabola with vertex (h, k)?

4. Based on your generalization, what rule can you write for a parabola with vertex at $(2, 3)$?

Algebra Activity Recording Sheet

(Use with the activity on page 308 in Lesson 6-4 of the Student Edition.)

Completing the Square

Materials: algebra tiles, equation mat

Model
Use algebra tiles to complete the square of each equation.

1. $x^2 + 2x - 4 = 0$

2. $x^2 + 4x + 1 = 0$

3. $x^2 - 6x = -5$

4. $x^2 - 2x = -1$

Algebra Activity Transparency Master

(Use with Algebra 2, Lesson 6-4)

Completing the Square

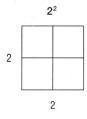

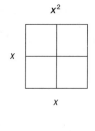

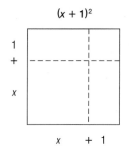

Fill in the blank to make a perfect square. What is the square root?

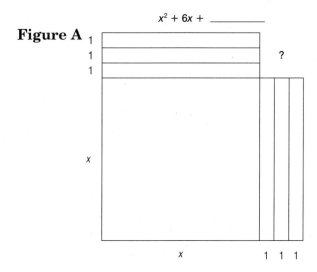

Figure A

$x^2 + 6x + \underline{\hspace{1cm}}$

Solve the equation by completing the square.

$$x^2 + 6x = 16$$

$$x^2 + 6x + \underline{\hspace{0.8cm}} = 16 + \underline{\hspace{0.8cm}}$$

$$(x + \underline{\hspace{0.8cm}})^2 =$$

$$x + \underline{\hspace{0.8cm}} = \pm$$

 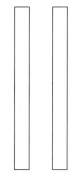 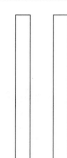   

Algebra Activity

(Use with Algebra 2, Lesson 6-4)

Completing the Square

Draw a diagram. Then fill in the blank to complete the square.

1. $x^2 + 8x +$ _____

2. $x^2 + 2x +$ _____

3. $x^2 + 4x +$ _____

4. $x^2 + 12x +$ _____

Solve each equation by completing the square.

Example: $x^2 + 4x = 12$
$$x^2 + 4x + 4 = 12 + 4$$
$$(x + 2)^2 = 16$$
$$x + 2 = \pm 4$$
$$x = \{-6, 2\}$$

5. $x^2 + 2x = 48$

6. $x^2 + 6x = 16$

7. $x^2 + 8x + 15 = 0$

8. $x^2 - 7x + 12 = 0$

9. $x^2 + 12x + 7 = 20$

10. $x^2 + 10x - 42 = -3$

Algebra Activity Transparency Master

(Use with Algebra 2, Lesson 6-6)

Quadratic Functions

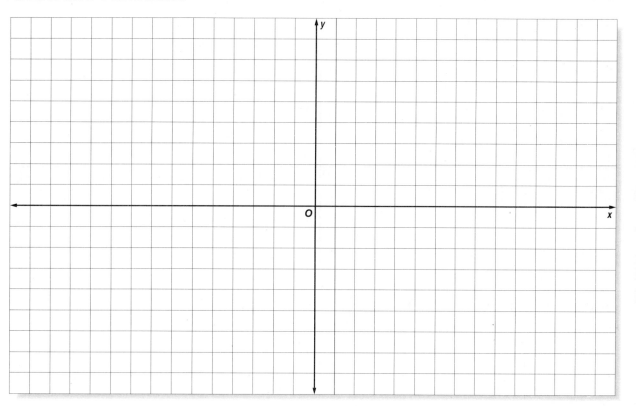

Figure A

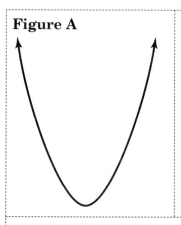

Figure B

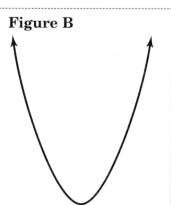

Figure C

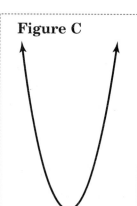

Figure D

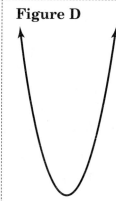

Figure E

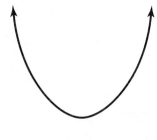

Figure F

Algebra Activity

(Use with Algebra 2, Lesson 6-6)

Quadratic Functions

Graph each parabola.

1. $f(x) = x^2$

2. $f(x) = x^2 + 5$

3. $f(x) = x^2 - 4$

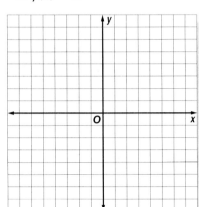 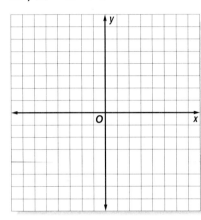 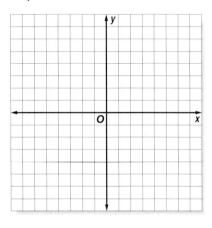

4. $f(x) = 4x^2$

5. $f(x) = \frac{1}{4}x^2$

6. $f(x) = -6x^2$

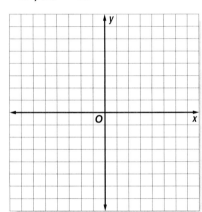 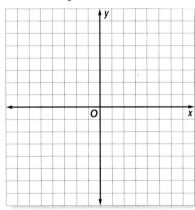 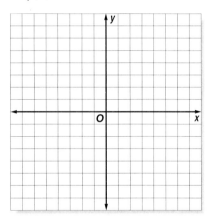

7. How are graphs 1, 2, and 3 similar? _____

8. How are graphs 4, 5, and 6 similar? _____

9. How do graphs 4 and 5 differ from graph 6? _____

_____

10. Give the vertex and the equation for the axis of symmetry for each graph.

a. _____ _____   **b** _____ _____
    vertex   axis of symmetry   vertex   axis of symmetry

c. _____ _____   **d.** _____ _____
    vertex   axis of symmetry   vertex   axis of symmetry

e. _____ _____   **f.** _____ _____
    vertex   axis of symmetry   vertex   axis of symmetry

11. Write each equation in the form $f(x) = a(x - h)^2 + k$. How do h and k relate to the vertex and the axis of symmetry?

7 Polynomial Functions
Teaching Notes and Overview

Mini-Project
Synthetic Substitution and Zeros
(p. 252 of this booklet)

Use With Lesson 7-4.

Objective Use synthetic substitution to find zeros of a function.

This Mini-Project requires students to use synthetic substitution to find the zeros of two functions and to write a detailed explanation of why synthetic substitution works. Ask students to work in pairs.

Answers

1. 1, 0, 1−10;
   1, 1, −2, 0;
   1, 2, −3, 0;
   1, 3, −2, −4;
   1, 4, 1, −6;
   1, 5, 6, 0;
   No need to substitute 2; zeros are −3, −2, and 1.
2. 1, −2, −1, 2, 0;
   1, −1, −5, 9, −12;
   1, 0, −7, 6, 0;
   1, −1, −7, −1, 6;
   1, 2, −5, −6, 0;
   1, 3, −1, −3, 0;
   No need to substitute 3; zeros are −3, −1, 1, and 2.

3. See students' explanations.

Algebra Activity
Exploring Iteration
(pp. 253–255 of this booklet)

Use With Lesson 7-7.

Objective Find and graph the first three iterates of a function.

There are two parts to this activity:

- The first part deals with finding the first three iterates of the function $f(x) = \frac{1}{2}x + 5$ for an initial value of $x_0 = 2$. Form groups of two students. Have them read and write down the work for each step. Discuss the

process and the first three iterates. Ask students to complete Exercises 1−4.

- The second part of the activity focuses on finding the first three iterates of the function $g(x) = 4x$ for an initial value of $x_0 = 0.25$, and then, drawing the graphical iteration. Before you go over Activity 2, discuss the four basic paths possible when a linear function is iterated.

As a class, have students graph the function $g(x) = 5x − 7$ and the function $f(x) = x$ on the same set of axes. Then draw the graphical iteration for $x_0 = 1$. State the slope of the linear function and tell what type of path the graphical iteration forms. The slope is 5 and the path staircases out.

Ask students to do the same for the function $g(x) = \frac{1}{4}x + 4$. The slope is $\frac{1}{4}$ and the path staircases in.

After discussing these exercises, you may want to talk about the process in general.

Step 1 Graph a function $g(x)$ and the line $f(x) = x$ on the coordinate plane.

Step 2 Choose an initial value, x_0, and locate the point $(x_0, 0)$.

Step 3 Draw a vertical line from $(x_0, 0)$ to the graph of $g(x)$. This will be the segment from the point $(x_0, 0)$ to $(x_0, g(x_0))$.

Step 4 Now draw a horizontal segment from this point to the graph of the line $f(x) = x$. This will be the segment from $(x_0, g(x_0))$ to $(g(x_0), g(x_0))$.

Repeat **Steps 1–4** for many iterations.

Tell students that they may think of the line $f(x) = x$ as a mirror that reflects each function value to become the input for the iteration of the function. The points at which the graph of the function $g(x)$ intersects the graph of the line $f(x) = x$ are called **fixed points**. If you try to iterate the initial value that corresponds to the x-coordinate of a fixed point, the iterates will all be the same.

Discuss the answers to Exercises 9−10. Ask a student from each group to read what they wrote for answers.

Teaching Algebra with Manipulatives

Answers

1. 1, 5, 25

2. 2, −3, 7

3. 4.6, 1.16, 2.54

4. 2.5, 4,38, 3.55

5. 4, staircases out

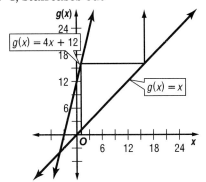

6. $\frac{3}{5}$, staircases in

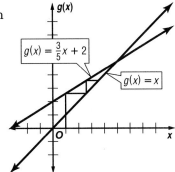

7. −2, spiral out

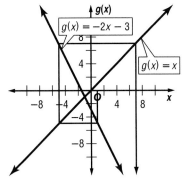

8. $-\frac{1}{3}$, spiral in

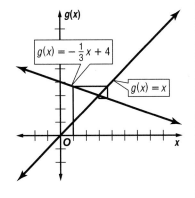

9. Sample answer: Functions whose slopes are positive form staircase paths; functions whose slopes are negative form spiral paths.

10. It initially forms a staircase pattern, then settles into a cyclical pattern.

Algebra Activity

Inverse Relations
(pp. 256–257 of this booklet)

Use With Lesson 7-8 as a follow-up activity.

Objectives Determine the inverse of a function or relation and graph a function and its inverse.

Materials

transparency of p. 256 from this booklet, cut on the dashed line
waxed paper
grid paper

Display the grid transparency on the overhead projector and graph $f(x) = x + 4$ using the Figure 1 template. Then show the inverse of the function using the Figure 2 template. Show students how the inverse is a reflection of the original graph. Have students draw these lines on their own graph paper and trace the graphs on waxed paper. Fold the waxed paper so the graphs overlap and crease. Unfold the waxed paper and lay it on the graph paper to discover that the crease is the axis of symmetry. Ask students to find the equation of the axis of symmetry. **y = x**

Repeat this activity using Figures 3 and 4 to graph $f(x) = x^2 + 3$ and its inverse.

Answers

1.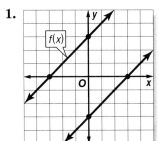

$y = x - 3$;
yes;
It passes the vertical line test.
yes;
$y = x$;

2.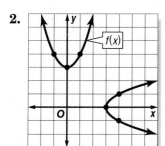

$y = \pm \sqrt{x - 3}$;
no;
Except for 3, the
domain values are
paired with two
range values.
yes;
$y = x$

3.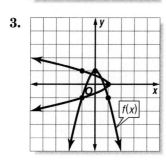

$y = \pm \dfrac{\sqrt{1 - x}}{2}$;
no;
Except for 1, the
domain values are
paired with two
range values.
yes;
$y = x$

4–8. See students' graphs for parts **a–d**.

4. no

5. no

6. An element of the domain is sometimes
paired with more than one element of the
range.

7. yes

8. The inverse is found by interchanging y and
x. This represents a reflection over $y = x$.

Algebra Activity Recording Sheet

Inverses of Functions
(p. 258 of this booklet)

Use With the activity on page 392 in Lesson
7-8 of the Student Edition.

Objective Use a geomirror to draw the
reflection of a function and write its equation.

Materials
grid paper
straightedge
geomirror

Students graph a function on grid paper then
use a geomirror to graph the reflection of the
function. They also write the equation of the
reflection and describe the relationship between
the two lines. Finally, students follow the same
procedures with a different function to
determine whether its inverse is also a
function.

Answers
See Teacher Wraparound Edition p. 392.

Algebra 2—Chapter 7

Mini-Project

(Use with Algebra 2, Lesson 7-4)

Synthetic Substitution and Zeros

Work with another student to complete the synthetic substitution chart. Then give the zeros of the function.

1. $f(x) = x^3 + 4x^2 + x - 6$

r	1	4	1	−6
−4				
−3				
−2				
−1				
0				
1				
2				

2. $f(x) = x^4 + x^3 - 7x^2 - x + 6$

r	1	1	−7	−1	6
−3					
−2					
−1					
0					
1					
2					
3					

3. Work together to write a detailed explanation of why synthetic substitution works.

         Teaching Algebra with Manipulatives

Algebra Activity
(Use with Algebra 2, Lesson 7-7)

Exploring Iteration

Each result of the iteration process is called an **iterate**. To interate a function $f(x)$, begin with a starting value x_0, find $f(x_0)$, and call the result x_1. Then find $f(x_1)$, and call the result x_2. Find $f(x_2)$ and call the result x_3, and so on.

Activity 1   **Find the first three iterates, x_1, x_2, and x_3, of the function $f(x) = \frac{1}{2}x + 5$ for an initial value of $x_0 = 2$.**

Step 1   To obtain the first iterate, find the value of the function for $x_0 = 2$.
$$f(x_0) = f(2)$$
$$= \frac{1}{2}(2) + 5 \text{ or } 6$$

Step 2   To obtain the second iterate x_2, substitute the function value for the first iterate, x_1, for x.
$$f(x_1) = f(6)$$
$$= \frac{1}{2}(6) + 5 \text{ or } 8$$

Step 3   Now find the third iterate, x_3, by substituting x_2 for x.
$$f(x_2) = f(8)$$
$$= \frac{1}{2}(8) + 5 \text{ or } 9$$

Therefore, the first three iterates for the function $f(x) = \frac{1}{2}x + 5$ for an initial value of $x_0 = 2$ are 6, 8, and 9.

Model

Find the first three iterates of each function using the given initial value. If necessary, round your answers to the nearest hundredth.

1. $g(x) = 5x; x_0 = 0.2$

2. $g(x) = -2x + 1; x_0 = -0.5$

3. $g(x) = 3 - 0.4x; x_0 = -4$

4. $g(x) = 3x - 0.5x^2; x_0 = 1$

Teaching Algebra with Manipulatives

Graphing iterations of a function can help you understand the process of iteration better. This process is called **graphical iteration**.
Four basic paths are possible when a linear function is iterated.

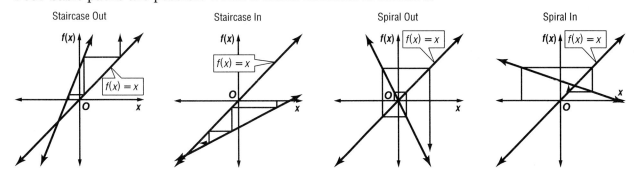

Activity 2   **Perform the graphical iteration on the function $g(x) = 4x$ for the first three iterates if the initial value is $x_0 = 0.25$. Which of the four types of paths does the iteration take?**

Step 1   To do the graphical iteration, first graph the functions $f(x) = x$ and $g(x) = 4x$.

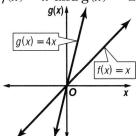

Step 2   Start at the point $(0.25, 0)$ and draw a vertical line to the graph of $g(x) = 4x$. From that point, draw a horizontal line to the graph of $f(x) = x$.

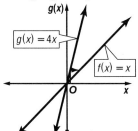

Step 3   Repeat the process from the point on $f(x) = x$. Then repeat again. The path of the iterations staircases out.

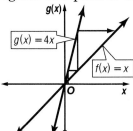

Draw

Graph each function and the function $f(x) = x$ on the same set of axes. Then draw the graphical iteration for $x_0 = 1$. State the slope of the linear function and tell what type of path the graphical iteration forms.

5. $g(x) = 4x + 12$

6. $g(x) = \frac{3}{5}x + 2$

7. $g(x) = -2x - 3$

8. $g(x) = -\frac{1}{3}x + 4$

Write

9. Write a paragraph explaining the relationship between the slope of a linear function and the type of path that the graphical iteration forms.

10. What type of path do you think is formed when you perform the graphical iteration on the function $f(x) = 5x - x^2$? How does it compare to the iteration of linear functions?

Teaching Algebra with Manipulatives

Algebra Activity Transparency Master

(Use with Algebra 2, Lesson 7-8)

Inverse Relations

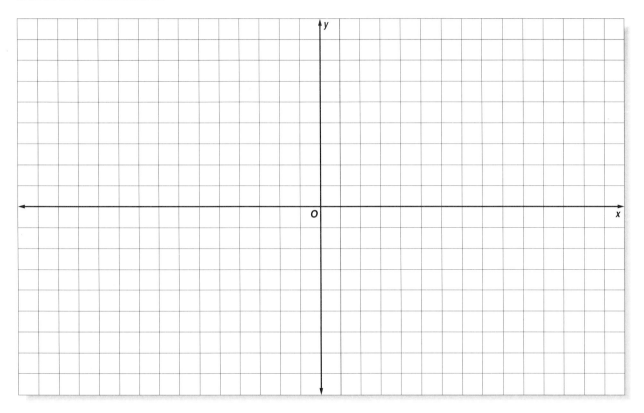

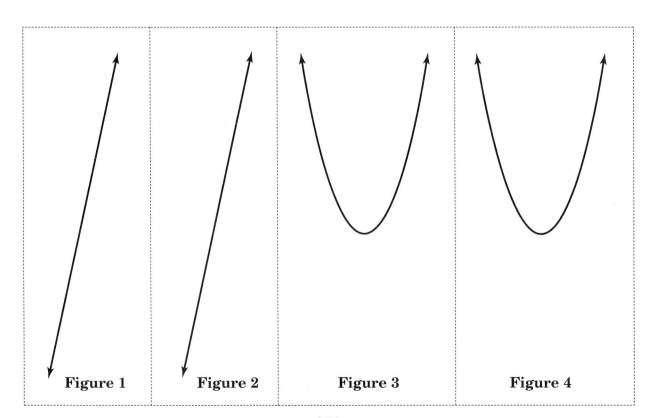

Figure 1   **Figure 2**   **Figure 3**   **Figure 4**

Algebra Activity

(Use with Algebra 2, Lesson 7-8)

Exploring Iteration

1. Graph $f(x) = x + 3$ and its inverse.

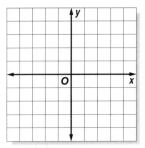

Equation of the inverse _____

Is the inverse a function? _____

Why or why not? _____

_____

Is it a transformation? _____

Axis of symmetry _____

2. Graph $f(x) = x^2 + 3$ and its inverse.

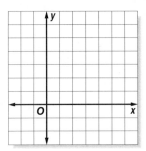

Equation of the inverse _____

Is the inverse a function? _____

Why or why not? _____

_____

Is it a transformation? _____

Axis of symmetry _____

3. Graph $f(x) = -2x^2 + 1$ and its inverse.

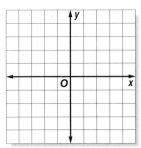

Equation of the inverse _____

Is the inverse a function? _____

Why or why not? _____

_____

Is it a transformation? _____

Axis of symmetry _____

Use your own grid paper and graph each function and its inverse.

a. $f(x) = 5$ **b.** $f(x) = 3x - 1$ **c.** $f(x) = (x + 2)^2$ **d.** $f(x) = -x$

4. Is the inverse of a linear equation always a function? _____

5. Is the inverse of any function always a function? _____

6. Why or why not? _____

7. Will the axis of symmetry always be the same? _____

8. Why or why not? _____

Algebra Activity Recording Sheet

(Use with the activity on page 392 in Lesson 7-8 of the Student Edition.)

Inverses of Functions

Materials: grid paper, straightedge, geomirror

Analyze

1. What is the equation of the drawn line?

2. What is the relationship between the line $y = 2x - 3$ and the line that you drew? Justify your answer.

3. Try this activity with the function $y = |x|$. Is the inverse also a function? Explain.

258

Conic Sections
Teaching Notes and Overview

Algebra Activity Recording Sheet

Midpoints and Distance Formulas in Three Dimensions
(p. 263 of this booklet)

Use With Lesson 8-1 as a follow-up activity. This corresponds to the activity on pages 417–418 in the Student Edition.

Objective Find the distance between two points and the midpoint of a segment in three-dimensional space.

Materials
none

This is a follow up activity from formulas for finding the midpoint of a segment and the distance between two points in two-dimensional space to three-dimensional space. As you go over the three-dimensional formulas used in Examples 1 and 2, you may want to display the two-dimensional formulas too. Ask students to compare and contrast the formulas.

Form groups of two or three students to complete Exercises 1–9. When the groups have finished these exercises, discuss their answers. Before assigning the remaining exercises, have students state the plan they will use to solve each exercise. Discuss their plans. As soon as the groups have completed Exercises 10–17, have them explain their solutions. Allow for a few minutes to ask the groups what they learned from working these exercises.

Answers
See Teacher Wraparound Edition pp. 417–418.

Algebra Activity Recording Sheet

Parabolas
(p. 264 of this booklet)

Use With the activity on page 421 in Lesson 8-2 of the Student Edition.

Objective Model and analyze the shapes of three parabolas.

Materials
waxed paper

This small group activity requires students to follow a step-by-step process that uses three pieces of waxed paper to make three different-shaped parabolas. Then students compare the shapes. Students are asked to decide how the distance between the focus and the directrix affect the shape of the parabola.

Answers
See Teacher Wraparound Edition p. 421.

Mini-Project

Conics
(p. 265 of this booklet)

Use With Lesson 8-2.

Objective Model and analyze parabolas.

Materials
clear acetate
grid paper

Divide students into groups to complete this Mini-Activity. Groups will need acetate paper and grid paper. At the conclusion of the project, discuss Exercise 5. Then ask each group to display their answers to Exercises 8–10. Require students to explain their work. Discuss Exercise 11. Show the graph of the equation.

Answers

1. See students' work.

2. parabola

3. See students' work.

4. See students' work.

5. The parabola becomes narrower.

6–10. See students' work.

11. $y = \frac{1}{16}x^2$

Algebra Activity Recording Sheet

Investigating Ellipses
(p. 266 of this booklet)

Use With Lesson 8-4 as a preview activity. This corresponds to the activity on page 432 in the Student Edition.

Objective Model, analyze, and make a conjecture about the ellipse.

Materials
two thumbtacks
cardboard
piece of string
rubber band
ruler*
* = available in Overhead Manipulative Resources

An ellipse can be constructed by using a pencil, two thumbtacks, a piece of string, and a piece of cardboard. Have groups follow Steps 1–4 to construct an ellipse. Before asking students to work the exercises, be sure each group has correctly completed the construction. Give each group a turn to share their answers. Require students to use the vocabulary *ellipse* and *focus/foci* in their explanation.

Answer
See Teacher Wraparound Edition p. 432.

Algebra Activity Recording Sheet

Locating Foci
(p. 267 of this booklet)

Use With the activity on page 437 in Lesson 8-4 of the Student Edition.

Objective Find the foci of an ellipse.

Material
grid paper
compass

This activity points out the connection between an ellipse and a circle. Form groups of two or three students to complete the four-step activity to locate the foci of an ellipse. Each group will need grid paper and a compass to draw a circle. As soon as the groups finish, discuss why this method works. Display the answers. Ask students if $y = -5$ could have been used in Step 3 instead of $y = 5$. **yes**

Answers
See Teacher Wraparound Edition p. 437.

Algebra Activity

Conic Sections
(pp. 268–269 of this booklet)

Use With Lesson 8-6.

Objective Graph and write equations for ellipses and hyperbolas.

Materials
classroom set of Algebra Activity worksheets
transparency master of Algebra Activity
waxed paper
scissors
compass

Before class cut a circle 5 inches to 6 inches in diameter out of waxed paper. Then cut the Algebra Activity transparency on the dashed line.

Step 1 Inside the circle, mark the center with point O and a second point A about 1 inch from the edge of the circle.

Step 2 Fold a crease in the circle, such that the edge of the circle touches point A.

Step 3   Repeat Step 2, making 20 to 25 folds. Notice that the creases form tangents to an ellipse.

Discuss the shape of the ellipse and its relationship to points A and O (the foci). Next, display the graph transparency of the grid and the ellipse to explain the exercises on the worksheet. Do the same for the hyperbola part of the worksheet. Have students complete the worksheet in small groups. When the groups are ready, have them share their results.

Answers

1. See students' work.

2a. $10; (5, 0), (-5, 0); \dfrac{x^2}{25} + \dfrac{y^2}{4} = 1$

2b. $10; (0, 5), (0, -5); \dfrac{x^2}{4} + \dfrac{y^2}{25} = 1$

2c. $10; (5, 2), (-5, 2); \dfrac{x^2}{25} + \dfrac{(y - 2)^2}{4} = 1$

2d. $10; (0, 1), (0, -9); \dfrac{x^2}{4} + \dfrac{(y + 4)^2}{25} = 1$

2e. $10; (-3, 3), (7, 3); \dfrac{(x - 2)^2}{25} + \dfrac{(y - 3)^2}{4} = 1$

2f. $10; (-1, 9), (-1, -1); \dfrac{(x + 1)^2}{4} + \dfrac{(y - 4)^2}{25} = 1$

3a. $(2, 0), (-2, 0); y = x, y = -x;$ $\dfrac{x^2}{4} - \dfrac{y^2}{4} = 1$

3b. $(0, 2), (0, -2); y = x, y = -x;$ $\dfrac{y^2}{4} - \dfrac{x^2}{4} = 1$

3c. $(1, 0), (5, 0); y = -x + 3, y = x - 3;$ $\dfrac{(x - 3)^2}{4} - \dfrac{y^2}{4} = 1$

3d. $(0, -2), (0, -6); y = x - 4, y = -x + 4;$ $\dfrac{(y + 4)^2}{4} - \dfrac{x^2}{4} = 1$

3e. $(-4, 3), (0, 3); y = x + 5, y = x - 1;$ $\dfrac{(x + 2)^2}{4} - \dfrac{(y - 3)^2}{4} = 1$

3f. $(1, 2), (1, 6); y = x + 3, y = -x + 5;$ $\dfrac{(y + 4)^2}{4} - \dfrac{(x - 1)^2}{4} = 1$

 Algebra Activity Recording Sheet

Conic Sections
(p. 270 of this booklet)

Use With Lesson 8-6 as a follow-up activity. This corresponds to the activity on pages 453–454 in the Student Edition.

Objective   Graph, model and analyze the parabola, ellipse, and hyperbola.

Materials
conic graph paper*
* = available in Overhead Manipulative Resources

The use of conic graph paper may be a first-time experience for students. Have them read the information about the conic graph paper at the top of the activity sheet. Then ask them questions. Point out that there are three activities. The first activity deals with a parabola, the second with an ellipse, and the third with a hyperbola. In small groups, have students do the parabola activity by following the directions listed. After the groups have completed the graph, discuss the results. Use the same process for the remaining two activities.

Algebra 2—Chapter 8

Ask students to complete the Exercises 1–3. Go over the results as soon as the groups have completed the work.

Answers
See Teacher Wraparound Edition pp. 453–454.

Algebra Activity Recording Sheet

(Use with the Lesson 8-1 Follow-Up Activity on pages 417–418 in the Student Edition.)

Midpoints and Distance Formulas in Three Dimensions

Materials: none

Exercises

Find the distance between each pair of points with the given coordinates.

1. $(2, 4, 5), (1, 2, 3)$

2. $(-1, 6, 2), (4, -3, 0)$

3. $(-2, 1, 7), (-2, 6, -3)$

4. $(0, 7, -1), (-4, 1, 3)$

Find the midpoint of each line segment with endpoints at the given coordinates.

5. $(2, 6, -1), (-4, 8, 5)$

6. $(4, -3, 2), (-2, 7, 6)$

7. $(1, 3, 7), (-4, 2, -1)$

8. $(2.3, -1.7, 0.6), (-2.7, 3.1, 1.8)$

9. The coordinates of one endpoint of a segment are $(4, -2, 3)$, and the coordinates of the midpoint are $(3, 2, 5)$. Find the coordinates of the other endpoint.

10. Two of the opposite vertices of a rectangular solid are at $(4, 1, -1)$ and $(2, 3, 5)$. Find the coordinates of the other six vertices.

11. Determine whether a triangle with vertices at $(2, -4, 2), (3, 1, 5)$, and $(6, -3, -1)$ is a right triangle. Explain.

The vertices of a rectangular solid are at $(-2, 3, 2), (3, 3, 2), (3, 1, 2),$ $(-2, 1, 2), (-2, 3, 6), (3, 3, 6), (3, 1, 6),$ and $(-2, 1, 6)$.

12. Find the volume of the solid.

13. Find the length of a diagonal of the solid.

14. Show that the point with coordinates $\left(\dfrac{x_1 + x_2}{2}, \dfrac{y_1 + y_2}{2}, \dfrac{z_1 + z_2}{2}\right)$ is equidistant from the points with coordinates (x_1, y_1, z_1) and (x_2, y_2, z_2).

15. Find the value of c so that the point with coordinates $(2, 3, c)$ is $3\sqrt{6}$ units from the point with coordinates $(-1, 0, 5)$.

The endpoints of a diameter of a sphere are at $(2, -3, 2)$ and $(-1, 1, -4)$.

16. Find the length of a radius of the sphere.

17. Find the coordinates of the center of the sphere.

Parabolas

Teaching Algebra with Manipulatives

Algebra 2—Chapter 8

Algebra Activity Recording Sheet

(Use with the activity on page 421 in Lesson 8-2 of the Student Edition.)

Parabolas

Materials: waxed paper

Analyze

Compare the shapes of the three parabolas. How does the distance between the focus and the directrix affect the shape of a parabola?

Mini-Project

(Use with Algebra 2, Lesson 8-2)

Conics

Complete the activity below.

1. Choose one of the lines on the grid below.

2. Find the points that are equidistant from the point and the line. Connect them with a smooth curve. What is the graph?

3. Using a different line, repeat the procedure above.

4. Using a third different line, repeat the procedure again.

5. As the line is closer to the point, what is the effect on the graph?

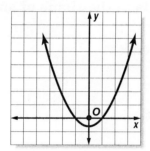

6. Trace each of your three graphs onto clear acetate. Include the line and the point.

7. Place the graph on $\frac{1}{4}$-inch grid paper, with the vertex on the origin and the line parallel to the x-axis.

Complete the following table for your three graphs.

	coordinate of the point	equation of the line	distance between the point and line	equation of the curve
8.				
9.				
10.				

11. Using the results above, what is the equation of the curve that is the set of points equidistant from the point $(0, 4)$ and the line $y = -4$?

Algebra Activity Recording Sheet

(Use with the Lesson 8-4 Preview Activity on page 432 in the Student Edition.)

Investigating Ellipses

Materials: two thumbtacks, cardboard, piece of string, rubber band, ruler

Model and Analyze
Follow the directions for Exercises 1 and 2 on page 432.

 2. How does this ellipse compare to the one in Exercise 1?

Make a Conjecture
**In Exercises 6–10, describe what happens to the shape of an
ellipse when each change is made.**

 6. The thumbtacks are moved closer together.

 7. The thumbtacks are moved farther apart.

 8. The length of the loop of string is increased.

 9. The thumbtacks are arranged vertically.

 10. One thumbtack is removed, and the string is looped around the
remaining thumbtack.

 11. Pick a point on one of the ellipses you have drawn. Use a ruler to
measure the distances from that point to the points where the
thumbtacks were located. Add the distances. Repeat for other
points on the same ellipse. What relationship do you notice?

 12. Could this activity be done with a rubber band instead of a piece of
string? Explain.

Algebra Activity Recording Sheet

(Use with the activity on page 437 in Lesson 8-4 of the Student Edition.)

Locating Foci

Materials: grid paper, compass

Make a Conjecture

Draw another ellipse and locate its foci using this method. Why does this method work?

Algebra Activity Transparency Master

(Use with Algebra 2, Lesson 8-6)

Conic Sections

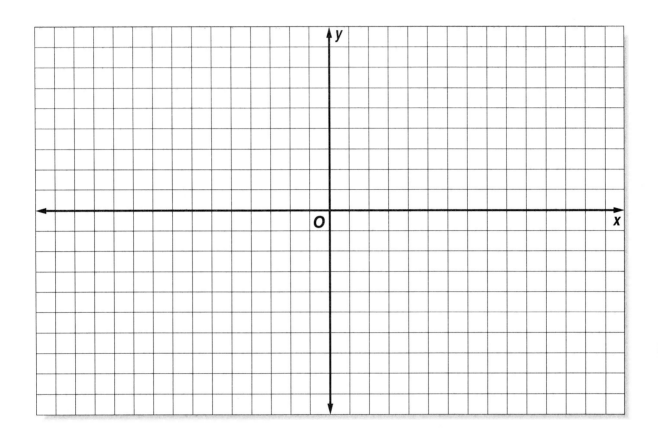

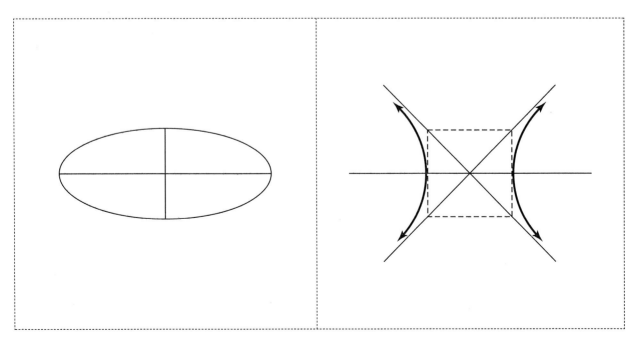

Algebra Activity

(Use with Algebra 2, Lesson 8-6)

Conic Sections

Complete the activity below.

Trace the following conic sections onto clear acetate.
Include the axes in your sketch.

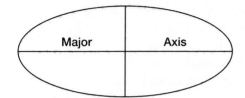

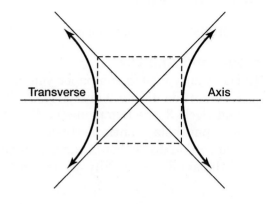

1. Mark coordinate axes on $\frac{1}{4}$-inch grid paper.

2. Place the ellipse with its center at the given point and its axis as
   indicated and complete the table below.

	Center	Major Axis	Length of Major Axis	Vertices	Equation
a.	(0, 0)	x-axis			
b.	(0, 0)	y-axis			
c.	(0, 2)	horizontal			
d.	(0, −4)	vertical			
e.	(2, 3)	horizontal			
f.	(−1, 4)	vertical			

3. Place the hyperbola with its center at the given point and its axis as
   indicated. Complete the table.

	Center	Transverse Axis	Vertices	Asymptotes	Equation
a.	(0, 0)	x-axis			
b.	(0, 0)	y-axis			
c.	(3, 0)	horizontal			
d.	(0, −4)	vertical			
e.	(−2, 3)	horizontal			
f.	(1, 4)	vertical			

Algebra Activity Recording Sheet

(Use with the Lesson 8-6 Follow-Up Activity on pages 453–454 in the Student Edition.)

Conic Sections

Materials: conic graph paper

Model and Analyze

1. Use the type of graph paper you used in Activity 1. Mark the intersection of line 0 and circle 2. Then mark the two points on line 1 and circle 3, the two points on line 2 and circle 4, and so on. Draw the new parabola. Continue this process and make as many parabolas as you can on one sheet of the graph paper. The focus is always the center of the small circle. Why are the resulting graphs parabolas?

2. In Activity 2, you drew an ellipse such that the sum of the distances from two fixed points was 13. Choose 10, 11, 12, 14, and so on, for that sum, and draw as many ellipses as you can on one piece of the graph paper.

   a. Why can you not start with 9 as the sum?

   b. What happens as the sum increases? decreases?

3. In Activity 3, you drew a hyperbola such that the difference of the distances from two fixed points was 7. Choose other numbers and draw as many hyperbolas as you can on one piece of graph paper. What happens as the difference increases? decreases?

 Mini-Project
Interpreting Powers of a Binomial Geometrically
(p. 272 of this booklet)

Use With Lesson 9-1.

Objective Interpret and analyze powers of a binomial geometrically.

This activity requires students to work in small groups to interpret and analyze two geometric models. Students are then asked to make other geometric models of their choosing to represent the products of binomials, and then, write an analysis of the models. As soon as the groups have completed Exercises 1–2, discuss their answers. In Exercise 1, take the opportunity to show that $(x + 4)^2 \neq x^2 + 16$. Also, in Exercise 2, that $(a + b)^3 \neq a^3 + b^3$. After completing Exercise 3, have the groups exchange models with one another and analyze them.

Answers

1. The area of the large square is $(x + 4)^2$. The areas of the component rectangles are x^2, $4x$, $4x$, and 16. Since the areas are equal, $(x + 4)^2 = x^2 + 8x + 16$.

2. The volume of the large cube is $(a + b)^3$. This cube consists of 8 rectangular prisms with the following volumes: a^3, b^3, $3ab^2$, and $3a^2b$. Thus, $(a + b)^3 = a^3 + b^3 + 3ab^2 + 3a^2b$.

3. See students' models and analyses.

 Algebra Activity Recording Sheet
Rational Functions
(p. 273 of this booklet)

Use With the activity on page 487 in Lesson 9-3 of the Student Edition.

Objective Use rational functions to graph real-life data.

Materials
balance
metric measuring cups
several various kinds of liquids
grid paper

Students use a balance to find the volumes of 200 grams of different liquids such as water, cooking oil, isopropyl alcohol, sugar water, and salt water. Then they find the density of each liquid and graph the data by plotting the points (volume, density) on a graph.

Answers
See Teacher Wraparound Edition p. 487.

Mini-Project

(Use with Algebra 2, Lesson 9-1)

Interpreting Powers of a Binomial Geometrically

Work in small groups to complete the activity.

1. Write an analysis of the following diagram as it relates to $(x + 4)^2$.

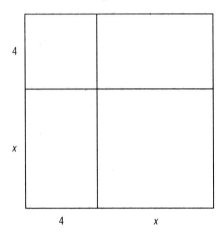

2. Write an analysis of the following diagram as it relates to $(a + b)^3$.

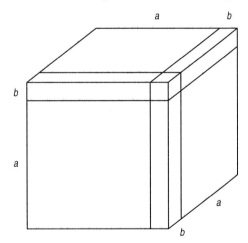

3. Make other geometric models to represent the products of binomials. Write an analysis of your models.

NAME _____ DATE _____ PERIOD _____

Algebra Activity Recording Sheet

(Use with the activity on page 487 in Lesson 9-3 of the Student Edition.)

Rational Functions

Materials: balance, metric measuring cups, several various liquids, grid paper

Analyze the Data

1. Graph the data by plotting the points (volume, density) on a graph. Connect the points.

2. From the graph, find the asymptotes.

Exponential and Logarithmic Relations
Teaching Notes and Overview

Algebra Activity Recording Sheet

Investigating Exponential Functions
(p. 275 of this booklet)

Use With Lesson 10-1 as a preview activity. This corresponds to the activity on page 522 in the Student Edition.

Objective Explore exponential functions by repeatedly cutting a piece of paper in half and graphing the results.

Materials
notebook paper   grid paper
scissors   calculator

Students repeatedly cut a sheet of paper in half and make a table of the results. They graph the data (number of cuts, number of sheets), and make conjectures about similar situations using different amounts of paper and number of cuts.

Answers
See Teacher Wraparound Edition p. 522.

Algebra Activity

Exponential Functions
(pp. 276–277 of this booklet)
Use With Lesson 10-1.

Objective Graph and interpret exponential functions.

Materials
classroom set of Algebra Activity worksheets
transparency master of Algebra Activity
60 dice

Using an overhead projector, display the transparency master and complete the chart using the data from the experiment below.

Step 1   Roll 60 dice. Then remove all dice rolled as a 6.

Step 2   Roll the remaining dice. Then remove the 6's again.

Repeat Steps 1 and 2 until all dice are eliminated, making sure to record the roll number and the number of dice rolled.

Plot the results and draw the curve.

Discuss the exponential functions and guide the class in deriving the formula for the experiment. $f(x) = 60\left(\frac{5}{6}\right)^n$, where n is the number of rolls, and $f(x)$ is the number of dice remaining.

The number of dice remaining after any roll equals the number of dice used in the next roll.

Overlap the transparency graph onto the curve drawn from the class experiment. Have students compare the two graphs.

You may want to conduct an extension to this activity. Change the experiment to $f(x) = 60\left(\frac{1}{2}\right)^n$ by tossing 60 coins and eliminating the "heads" toss. Discuss applications of exponential growth and decay. Ask interested students to do an investigation related to the latter and share the results of their work with the class.

Answers
1. See students' graphs; $\left(1, \frac{1}{3}\right), \left(2, \frac{1}{9}\right), (0, 1)$
2. See students' graphs; $(1, 3), (2, 9), (3, 27),$ $(0, 1)$
3. See students' graphs; $\left(1, \frac{1}{2}\right), \left(2, \frac{1}{4}\right), (0, 1)$
4. See students' graphs; $(1, 2), (2, 4), (3, 8), (0, 1)$

Mini-Project

Graceful Numbering of Graphs
(p. 278 of this booklet)
Use With Lesson 10-6.

Objective Find graceful numberings for graphs.

Have students read and study the information about graceful numbering at the top of the Mini-Project worksheet. Then ask questions about the meaning of a graceful numbering of a graph. Be sure they understand that a graceful numbering of a graph requires that the greatest number used to label a dot be equal to the total number of segments. Have groups of two students work on this activity.

Answers
1–3. See students' work.

Algebra Activity Recording Sheet

(Use with the Lesson 10-1 Preview Activity on page 522 in the Student Edition.)

Investigating Exponential Functions

Materials: notebook paper, scissors, grid paper, calculator

Analyze the Data

1. Write a list of ordered pairs (x, y), where x is the number of cuts and y is the number of sheets in the stack. Notice that the list starts with the ordered pair $(0, 1)$, which represents the single sheet of paper before any cuts were made.

2. Continue the list, beyond the point where you stopped cutting, until you reach the ordered pair for 7 cuts. Explain how you calculated the last y values for your list, after you had stopped cutting.

3. Plot the ordered pairs in your list on a coordinate grid. Be sure to choose a scale for the y-axis so that you can plot all of the points.

4. Describe the pattern of the points you have plotted. Do they lie on a straight line?

Make a Conjecture

5. Write a function that expresses y as a function of x.

6. Use a calculator to evaluate the function you wrote in Exercise 5 for $x = 8$ and $x = 9$. Does it give the correct number of sheets in the stack after 8 and 9 cuts?

7. Notebook paper usually stacks about 500 sheets to the inch. How thick would your stack of paper be if you had been able to make 9 cuts?

8. Suppose each cut takes about 5 seconds. If you had been able to keep cutting, you would have made 36 cuts in three minutes. At 500 sheets to the inch, make a conjecture as to how thick you think the stack would be after 36 cuts.

9. Use your function from Exercise 5 to calculate the thickness of your stack after 36 cuts. Write your answer in miles.

Teaching Algebra with Manipulatives

Algebra 2—Chapter 10

Algebra Activity Transparency Master

(Use with Algebra 2, Lesson 10-1)

Exponential Functions

Roll No.	No. of Dice Rolled

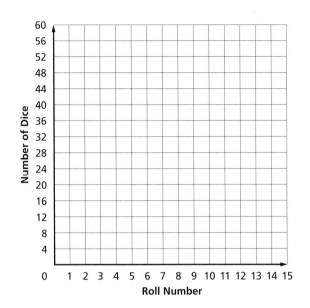

Roll No.	No. of Dice Rolled
1	60
2	50
3	41.67
4	34.73
5	28.94
6	24.12
7	20.1
8	16.75
9	13.96
10	11.63
11	9.69
12	8.08
13	6.73
14	5.6
15	4.67

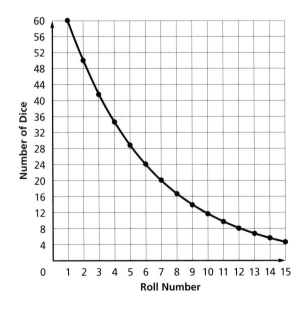

Algebra Activity

(Use with Algebra 2, Lesson 10-1)

Exponential Functions

Make a table of values and graph the following exponential functions.

1. $f(x) = \left(\dfrac{1}{3}\right)^x$

x	$f(x)$

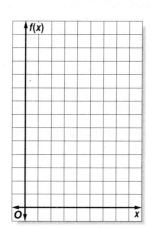

2. $f(x) = 3^x$

x	$f(x)$

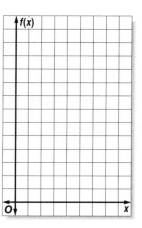

3. $f(x) = \left(\dfrac{1}{2}\right)^x$

x	$f(x)$

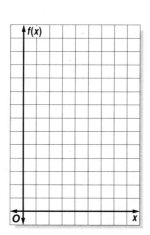

4. $f(x) = 2^x$

x	$f(x)$

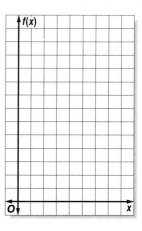

Answer the following questions about the graphs above.

5. How do the graphs of Exercises 1 and 3 compare?

6. How do the graphs of Exercises 2 and 4 compare?

7. Which graphs might represent the rate of depreciation of a car over a period of several years?

8. Which graphs might represent the growth rate of bacteria over a period of time?

Algebra 2—Chapter 10

Mini-Project

(Use with Algebra 2, Lesson 10-6)

Graceful Numbering of Graphs

The dots and segments joining the dots in the graphs below are to be numbered by the following rules.

(1) Each dot is to be numbered with a different nonnegative integer.

(2) Each segment is to be labeled with the positive difference of the numbers for the dots that it connects. These numbers must all be different.

A graceful numbering of the graph requires that the greatest number used to label a dot be equal to the total number of segments.

Work with your group to see if you can find graceful numberings for these graphs.

1.

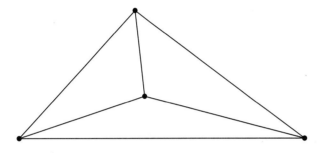

2.

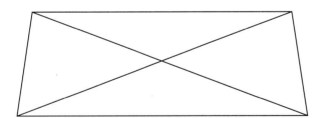

3.

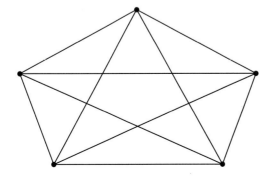

11 Sequences and Series
Teaching Notes and Overview

Mini-Project
Sequences
(p. 282 of this booklet)

Use With Lesson 11-1.

Objective Find the missing term of an infinite sequence. Find the total number of rectangles formed from an $n \times n$ grid.

Materials
none

Have students work in groups of two or three to find the missing term for each infinite sequence in Exercises 1–8. In addition, students are asked to use their answers from Exercises 1–8 to form a special sequence of eight numbers. Then they list the next three terms of the sequence.

Exercises 9–11 deal with finding the total number of rectangles formed when given a 1×1, a 2×2, and a 3×3 grid. Exercise 12 requires them to generalize the process by writing a rule to predict how many rectangles are formed by an $n \times n$ grid. The infinite sequence is 1, 9, 32, and so on. Ask students to find the 4th term and 5th term of this sequence.
4395; 5494

Answers

1. 15   2. −1

3. 24   4. 35

5. 3   6. 0

7. 8   8. 48
   −1, 0, 3, 8, 15, 24, 35, 48; 63, 80, 99

9. 1

10. 9

11. 32

12. Number of rectangles = $n^3 + n^2 - n - 1$

Algebra Activity Recording Sheet
Arithmetic Sequences
(p. 283 of this booklet)

Use With the activity on page 580 in Lesson 11-1 of the Student Edition.

Objective Draw a series of figures on isometric dot paper to illustrate and complete an arithmetic sequence.

Materials
isometric dot paper*
* = available in Overhead Manipulative Resources

Using isometric dot paper, students draw the fourth figure in the given pattern. Next, they find the volume of all four figures and write an equation that gives the volume of Figure n. Finally, students use the equation they wrote to find the volume of the twelfth figure in the sequence.

Answers
See Teacher Wraparound Edition p. 580.

Algebra Activity Recording Sheet
Fractals
(p. 284 of this booklet)

Use With Lesson 11-6 as a follow-up activity. This corresponds to the activity on page 611 in the Student Edition.

Objective Collect and analyze data about a fractal called the **von Koch snowflake**.

Materials
isometric dot paper*
* = available in Overhead Manipulative Resources

On the Algebra Recording Sheet, have students read about fractals. Pass out dot paper. Have students follow along with the illustration and draw the two stages of the construction of a fractal called the *von Koch snowflake*. You may want to show the two stages on a whiteboard, an easel, or on a transparency.

Teaching Algebra with Manipulatives

Algebra 2—Chapter 11

Discuss the completed parts of the table in Exercise 1. Ask students questions about the table to check on their understanding. Complete the missing parts of the table as a class.

Form groups of two or three to complete Exercises 2–7. You may want to have the groups complete two of the exercises, then discuss the answers as a class. Then have them complete two more and discuss the answers and so on.

Encourage students to research other fractals and share their findings with the class.

Answers
See Teacher Wraparound Edition p. 611.

Algebra Activity Recording Sheet

Special Sequences
(p. 285 of this booklet)

Use With the activity on page 607 in Lesson 11-6 of the Student Edition.

Objective Model, analyze, and make a conjecture about the *Towers of Hanoi* game.

Materials
provide each group of students with the following:
penny
nickel
dime
quarter

Point out to students that the object of the *Towers of Hanoi* game is to move a stack of n coins from one position to another in the fewest number of a_n of moves. Go over the rules with the students.

Divide the class into groups. Provide a penny, nickel, dime, and quarter or a facsimile of these for each group. Ask each group to keep a record of the moves required to complete each exercise. As soon as the groups have completed the exercises, discuss the answers. Have students explain how they solved the problem.

Encourage students to find other mathematical games and to share them with the rest of the class.

Answers
See Teacher Wraparound Edition p. 607.

Algebra Activity

Fractal Cut-Outs
(pp. 286–287 of this booklet)

Use With Lesson 11-6 as an extension.

Objective Make a visual model of a self-similar structure.

Materials
4 sheets of 8.5″-by-11″ plain paper
ruler
scissors
colored pencils or markers

Have students work in pairs. Remind students to measure and cut carefully to obtain the best results. You may want to give each pair of students extra paper in case they make an error in cutting. Make sure students realize the pattern of the placement of the cut and the length of the cut before attempting Cards 3 and 4. The cut is always one-fourth the width of the fold and the length of the cut is one-half of the height of the folded section.

Students need to sharply crease their folds in order to get the desired effect, especially on Cards 3 and 4. You may want students to attach their cards to poster board to make a three-dimensional display of their work.

Answers

1. 1, 3, 7, 15

2. (Card, Area): (1, 20), (2, 25), (3, 26.25), (4, 26.5625), (5, 26.640625), (6, 26.660156), (7, 26.665039), (8, 26.66626), (9, 26.666565), (10, 26.666641)

3. Sample answer: The number of boxes for Card 1 is 1. Then for each card, you add a power or 2. Card 2 = $1 + 2^1$ or 3. Card $3 = 1 + 2^2$ or 5, Card 4 = $1 + 2^3$ or 7, and so on. Card $n = 1 + 2^{n-1}$.
   Alternate answer: The number of boxes is $2^n - 1$, where n is the card number.

4. 1023

5. Sample answer: It appears that the surface area of the protruding part is approaching 26.67 or $26\frac{2}{3}$.

6.

Card	Volume (in³)
1	1
2	1.25
3	1.3125
4	1.328125
5	1.3320313
6	1.3330078
7	1.333252
8	1.333313
9	1.3333283
10	1.3333321

It appears that the volume is approaching 1.33 or $1\frac{1}{3}$ in³.

Extension

Make a different set of four fractal cards using different fractions than one fourth and one half for the cuts. Compare your table and ratios with the ones from Exercises 2 and 6.

Algebra 2—Chapter 11

Mini-Project

(Use with Algebra 2, Lesson 11-1)

Sequences

Fill in the missing terms for each infinite sequence.

1. 3, 7, 11, _____, 19,...

2. $\frac{4}{3}$, _____, $\frac{3}{4}$, $-\frac{9}{16}$,....

3. 3, 6, 12, _____, 48,...

4. 175, _____, 7, $\frac{7}{5}$,...

5. _____, $\sqrt{3}$, 1,...

6. 10, 5, _____, -5, -10,...

7. 2, _____, 18, 32,...

8. 2, 4, 12, _____, 240,...

Arrange your answers for Exercises 1–8 to form a special sequence of eight numbers. Then list the next three terms of your sequence.

_____, _____, _____, _____, _____, _____, _____, _____,

List the next three terms of the sequence.

_____, _____, _____

For each of the following $n \times n$ square grids, find the total number of rectangles formed.

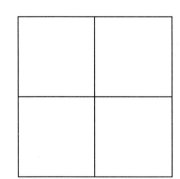 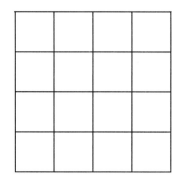

9. _____

10. _____

11. _____

12. Use the results for Exercises 9–11 to write a rule to predict how many rectangles are formed by a 4×4 grid, a 5×5 grid, and so on.

Algebra Activity Recording Sheet

(Use with the activity on page 580 in Lesson 11-1 of the Student Edition.)

Arithmetic Sequences

Materials: isometric dot paper

Model and Analyze

1. Based on the pattern, draw the fourth figure on a piece of isometric dot paper.

2. Find the volumes of the four figures.

3. Suppose the number of cubes in the pattern continues. Write an equation that gives the volume of Figure n.

4. What would the volume of the twelfth figure be?

Algebra 2—Chapter 11

Algebra Activity Recording Sheet

(Use with the Lesson 11-6 Follow-Up Activity on page 611 in the Student Edition.)

Fractals

Materials: isometric dot paper

Model and Analyze

1. Complete the table. Draw Stage 3, if necessary.

Stage	1	2	3	4
Number of Segments	3	12		
Length of each Segments	9	3		
Perimeter	27	36		

2. Write recursive formulas for the number s_n of segments in Stage n, the length l_n of each segment in Stage n, and the perimeter P_n of Stage n.

3. Write nonrecursive formulas for s_n, l_n, and P_n.

4. What is the perimeter of the von Koch snowflake? Explain.

5. Explain why the area of the von Koch snowflake can be represented by the infinite series $\frac{81\sqrt{3}}{4} + \frac{27\sqrt{3}}{4} + 3\sqrt{3} + \frac{4\sqrt{3}}{3} + \ldots$.

6. Find the sum of the series in Exercise 5. Explain your steps.

7. Do you think the results of Exercises 4 and 6 are contradictory? Explain.

Algebra Activity Recording Sheet

(Use with the activity on page 607 in Lesson 11-6 of the Student Edition.)

Special Sequences

Materials: penny, nickel, dime, quarter

Model and Analyze

1. Draw three circles on a sheet of paper. Place a penny on the first circle. What is the least number of moves required to get the penny to the second circle?

2. Place a nickel and a penny on the first circle, with the penny on top. What is the least number of moves that you can make to get the stack to another circle? (Remember, a nickel cannot be placed on top of a penny.)

3. Place a nickel, penny, and dime on the first circle. What is the least number of moves that you can take to get the stack to another circle?

Make a Conjecture

4. Place a quarter, nickel, penny, and dime on the first circle. Experiment to find the least number of moves needed to get the stack to another circle. Make a conjecture about a formula for the minimum number a_n of moves required to move a stack of n coins.

Teaching Algebra with Manipulatives

Algebra Activity

(Use with Algebra 2, Lesson 11-6)

Investigating Fractal Cut-Outs

Materials 4 sheets of 8.5″-by-11″ plain paper, cut to measure 8″ by 10″
ruler
scissors
colored pencils or markers

Collect the Data

Fractals are self-similar shapes in which you can find replicas of an entire shape or object embedded over and over again in different sizes. Follow these directions and diagrams to make five fractal cards.

Step 1 Fold one of the 8″-by-10″ sheets of paper in half. (Figure 1.2) Measure and make cuts on the fold. (Figure 1.3)

Figure 1.1   **Figure 1.2**   **Figure 1.3**

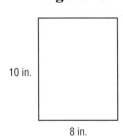 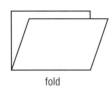 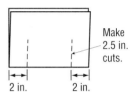

Step 2 Fold the cut section up as shown and crease sharply (Figure 2.1) Then unfold the paper and refold the creases in the opposite direction. Fold it so a box protrudes as shown in Figure 2.2. Color the two sides of the protruding box blue. This is **Fractal Card 1**.

Figure 2.1   **Figure 2.2**

    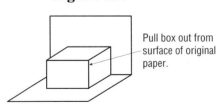

Step 3 To make **Fractal Card 2,** take a second sheet of paper and make a fractal card identical to Fractal Card 1 by repeating Steps 1 and 2 above, but do not unfold the paper in Step 2.

Step 4 With the inner portion folded up as shown, measure and make two more cuts. Notice that the distance from the edge to each cut is one-fourth the width of the folded portion and the cuts are one-half the distance from the fold to the top of the paper.

Step 5 Fold and crease the new section. Unfold the paper and refold the creases in the opposite direction. Fold all the box shapes out. Color all the protruding sides red.

Step 6 With a third piece of paper create **Fractal Card 3**. Use the folding and cutting directions from Steps 3 through 5, but do not unfold the paper. Fold the center flap up to the top and cut slits that are 0.75 inches long to create Fractal Card 3. Color the protruding sides for Fractal Card 3 yellow.

Step 7 Repeat the pattern of folding and cutting another step to create **Fractal Card 4**. Color the protruding boxes green.

Analyze the Data

1. List the total number of boxes that protrude on each fractal card.

Card 1 _____ Card 2 _____ Card 3 _____ Card 4 _____

2. Find the area of the colored sections on Fractal Cards 1 through 4. Then find a pattern to help you complete the table.

Fractal Card	Area of Colored Section (in^2)	
1	$2(2.5 \cdot 4) =$	
2		
3		
4		
5		
6		
7		
8		
9		
10		

Make a Conjecture

3. Describe the pattern shown in the number of protruding boxes for each card. Write a formula for finding the number of boxes for any fractal card where n is the number of the card.

4. How many boxes would protrude from Fractal Card 10?

5. Explain any patterns that you see in the table for Exercise 2.

6. Add a third column to the table in Exercise 2. Find the ratio: *area of colored portion of given card* to *area of colored portion of Fractal Card 1*. Describe any patterns in these values.

Algebra 2—Chapter 11

Probability and Statistics
Teaching Notes and Overview

Algebra Activity Recording Sheet

Area Diagrams
(p. 291 of this booklet)

Use With the activity on page 651 in Lesson 12-4 of the Student Edition.

Objective Model the probability of two events occurring at the same time using an area diagram.

Materials
none

This activity involves using an area diagram to model the probability of the two events, namely, colored clips and metallic clips, at the same time. Explain how the area diagram is constructed. The 1 red and three blue clips represent the colored clips. The probability of drawing a red clip (1) from the colored clips (4) is $\frac{1}{4}$, and drawing a blue clip (3) from the colored clips (4) is $\frac{3}{4}$. The probability of drawing a gold clip (1) from the metallic clips (3) is $\frac{1}{3}$, and drawing a silver clip (2) from the metallic clips (3) is $\frac{2}{3}$. Point out that rectangle A represents drawing 1 silver clip and 1 blue clip, that is, $\frac{2}{3}$ by $\frac{3}{4}$. Before you separate the class into groups to complete the exercises, you may want to go over what rectangles B, C, and D represent.

Answers
See Teacher Wraparound Edition p. 651.

Algebra Activity

Probability
(pp. 292–293 of this booklet)

Use With Lesson 12-4.

Objective Find the probability of a compound event.

Materials
classroom set of Algebra Activity worksheets
transparency master of Algebra Activity
3 coins per group of students

Pass out the Algebra Activity worksheets and 2 coins to each group. Ask the groups of students to complete Exercise 1 on the worksheet. Then record each group's results on the transparency master.

Compare the total number of HHs to the total number of tosses. Use ratios and percents for this comparison and record the results on the transparency.

Make a scatter plot of each group's results on the transparency. Draw a line that is suggested by the points.

Use the tree diagram on the transparency to illustrate possible outcomes from the toss of two coins. Have students complete Exercises 2 and 3.

As an extension, ask students to predict outcomes for the toss of 3 coins and perform a similar experiment. Have students compare their experimental results to this theoretical value.

Answers

1. See students' work.

2a. $\frac{1}{4}$

2b. $\frac{9}{20}$

2c. males 30 and over

3a. $\frac{3}{10}$

3b. $\frac{9}{40}$

3c. tells where or where not to concentrate their efforts

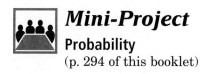

Mini-Project

Probability
(p. 294 of this booklet)

Use With Lesson 12-8.

Objective Make predictions using probability.

Materials
provide the following for each group:
5 coins
2 dice
deck of 52 cards
"bag" of 6 red chips, 2 white chips, 1 blue chip

Discuss the example and the completion of the chart as a class. Then give each group the materials necessary to complete this activity on making predictions using probability. As soon as the groups have finished Exercises 1–2, compare both your results and the class average to your prediction. Then have each group complete Exercise 3. Discuss both Situations 1 and 2 as a class. Have students read and discuss their conclusions based on their own results, the class average, and the predicted probability.

Answers

1–3. See students' work.

Algebra Activity Recording Sheet

Simulations
(p. 295 of this booklet)

Use With Lesson 12-8 as an extension activity. This corresponds to the activity on page 681 in the Student Edition.

Objective Use a simulation to solve a real-life situation.

Material
provide die for each group

This activity deals with using probability to conduct a simulation to solve a problem. Students are given a cereal problem. They work in pairs to Collect the Data by following a four-step process. Next, the groups begin to Analyze the Data by creating two different statistical graphs. Then students find the mean, median, maximum, minimum, and standard deviation of the data. Next, the groups combine their results. The remaining exercises require students to Make a Conjecture about further investigations of the data with defined alterations. You may want to discuss the work after the groups have completed Exercises 1–3 and then after Exercises 4–7.

Answers
See Teacher Wraparound Edition p. 681.

Algebra Activity Recording Sheet

Testing Hypotheses
(p. 296 of this booklet)

Use With Lesson 12-9 as an extension activity. This corresponds to the activity on page 686 in the Student Edition.

Objective Test a hypothesis to determine whether it is true or false using a five-step process.

Materials
ruler*
clock
* = available in Overhead Manipulative Resources

Go over the five-step process for testing a hypothesis. Then follow the process spelled out under Collect the Data. The hypothesis tested: *People react to sound and touch at the same rate*. Half of the class will investigate the time it takes to react when someone is told the ruler has dropped. The other half will measure the time it takes to react when the catcher is alerted by touch.

Ask students to work in groups to complete Exercises 1–3. As soon as they complete these exercises, discuss the answers. Exercise 4 deals with designing an experiment to test a given hypothesis. They may need assistance. Emphasize the importance of following the five-step process for testing a hypothesis. Have the groups share and exchange their findings.

Answers
See Teacher Wraparound Edition p. 686.

Algebra Activity Recording Sheet

(a reproduction of the activity on page 651 in Lesson 12-4 of the Student Edition)

Area Diagrams

Materials: none

Model and Analyze

1. Find the areas of rectangles A, B, C, and D, and explain what each area represents.

2. What is the probability of choosing a red paper clip and a silver paper clip?

3. What are the length and width of the whole square? What is the area? Why does the area need to have this value?

4. Make an area diagram that represents the probability of each outcome if you spin each spinner once. Label the diagram and describe what the area of each rectangle represents.

Algebra Activity Transparency Master

(Use with Algebra 2, Lesson 12-4)

Probability

Group No.	1	2	3	4	5	6	7	8	9	10	TOTAL
HH											
not HH											
% win											

Scatter Plot

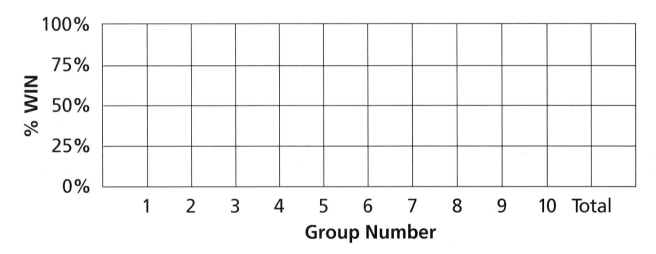

Tree Diagram
2 Coins

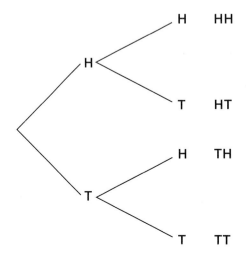

Algebra Activity

(Use with Algebra 2, Lesson 12-4)

Probability

1. Toss two coins 25 times. Tally each result as Heads-Heads (HH) or not Heads-Heads in the chart to the right.

$\dfrac{\text{Number of HH}}{\text{Total Tosses}}$ = _____% win

Result	Tally
Heads-Heads	
not Head-Heads	

2. A sample of 200 customers in a store gave the following results.

GENDER

		Male	Female	Total
	Under 30	60	50	110
AGE	**30 & Over**	80	10	90
	Total	140	60	200

a. What is the probability a customer is under 30 and female?

b. What is the probability a customer is 30 or over?

c. If you were the manager of this store, what population would you target with your merchandise?

3. Public reactions to a new school tax levy are recorded below.

		For	Against	Did Not Vote	Total
	Under 20	240	40	40	320
AGE	**20–40**	100	120	60	280
	Over 40	100	80	20	200
	Total	440	240	120	800

a. What is the probability a person under 20 will vote for the levy?

b. What is the probability a person over 40 will vote at all?

c. How can the results of the poll be used by political parties to encourage more people to vote for or against the school tax levy?

Algebra 2—Chapter 12

Mini-Project

(Use with Algebra 2, Lesson 12-8)

Probability

In groups, complete the laboratory activity below.

Materials: 5 coins, 2 dice, deck of 52 cards, "bag" of 6 red chips, 2 white chips, and 1 blue chip for each group.

Make predictions using probability for the outcomes of the situations below. Then actually simulate the situation through experimentation, filling in the chart. Compare both your results and the class average to your prediction.

Probability Prediction		Experimentation		Comparison (+, −)	
Situation	Your Prediction	Number of Favorable Outcomes	Class Average	Your Number to Prediction	Class Average to Prediction
Example How often will only 3 heads show when 5 coins are tossed together 16 times?	10	7	9	−3	−1
1. How often will the sum of 2 dice be 7 when they are tossed together 18 times?					
2. One card is selected from a deck of 52. If 13 cards are drawn how often will the card be a red card or an 8?					

3. Write a conclusion for each experiment based on your own results, the class average, and the predicted probability.

   a. Situation 1:

   b. Situation 2:

Algebra Activity Recording Sheet

(Use with the activity on page 681 in Lesson 12-8 of the Student Edition.)

Simulations

Materials: die

Analyze the Data

1. Create two different statistical graphs of the data collected for 25 trials.

2. Determine the mean, median, maximum, minimum, and standard deviation of the total number of boxes needed in the 25 trials.

3. Combine the small-group results and determine the mean, median, maximum, minimum, and standard deviation of the number of boxes required for all the trials conducted by the class.

Make a Conjecture

4. If you carry out 25 additional trials, will your results be the same as in the first 25 trials? Explain.

5. Should the small-group results or the class results give a better idea of the average number of boxes required to get a complete set of superheroes? Explain.

6. If there were 8 superheroes instead of 6, would you need to buy more boxes of cereal or fewer boxes of cereal on average?

7. What if one of the 6 prizes was more common than the other 5? For instance, suppose that one prize, Amazing Amy, appears in 25% of all the boxes and the other 5 prizes are equally and randomly distributed among the remaining 75% of the boxes? Design and carry out a new simulation to predict the average number of boxes you would need to buy to get a complete set. Include some measures of central tendency and dispersion with your data.

Algebra 2—Chapter 12

Algebra Activity Recording Sheet

(Use with the activity on page 686 in Lesson 12-9 of the Student Edition.)

Testing Hypotheses

Materials: ruler, clock

Analyze

State the null and alternative hypotheses for each conjecture.

1. A teacher feels that playing classical music during a math test will cause the test scores to change (either up or down). In the past, the average test score was 73.

2. An engineer thinks that the mean number of defects can be decreased by using robots on an assembly line. Currently, there are 18 defects for every 1000 items.

3. A researcher is concerned that a new medicine will cause pulse rates to rise dangerously. The mean pulse rate for the population is 82 beats per minute.

Make a Conjecture

4. Design an experiment to test the following hypothesis.
   Pulse rates increase 20% after moderate exercise.

13 Trigonometric Functions
Teaching Notes and Overview

Algebra Activity
Indirect Measurement
(pp. 299–300 of this booklet)

Use With Lesson 13-1.

Objective Use indirect measurement as an application of trigonometric functions.

Material
classroom set of Algebra Activity worksheets
transparency master of Algebra Activity
each pair of students needs the following:
protractor*
5″ by 7″ index card
straw
paper clip
transparent tape
kite string
scientific calculator*
* = available in Overhead Manipulative Resources

Prior to class, assemble a model of the hypsometer according to the transparency master.

Display the transparency on the overhead projector. Have pairs of students assemble hypsometers as shown in the diagram. Tell students to make sure the string hangs freely to create a plumb line. If protractors are not available, use the protractor model at the bottom of the transparency.

Ask students to practice finding a horizontal line and the line of sight, and reading the hypsometer angle of inclination.

To solve for the height of the object use the following:
$$\tan (\text{angle sighted}) = \frac{\text{height} - d}{\text{horizontal distance}}$$
where d represents the distance from the ground to a person's eye level. Have the pairs of students complete Exercises 1 and 2 on the Algebra Activity worksheet. Go outside and have students complete the remaining exercises.

Answers

1. Approximately 15.5 ft

2. Approximately 19.3 m

3–8. See students' work.

Algebra Activity Recording Sheet
Investigating Regular Polygons Using Trigonometry
(p. 301 of this booklet)

Use With Lesson 13-2 as a follow-up activity. This corresponds to the activity on page 716 in the Student Edition.

Objective Use trigonometry to find relationships between the angle measures, number of sides, and length of apothems of regular polygons.

Materials
compass
protractor
straightedge

Students inscribe regular polygons with the number of sides ranging from three to ten in circles with radius one inch. Using an angle formed in the center of the polygon and trigonometry, students find the length of the apothem of each polygon. This, along with the measure of the angle, is recorded in a table. Students then use the table to identify and describe patterns and relationships. Finally, they make conjectures and write formulas based on similar situations with slightly different criteria.

Answers
See Teacher Wraparound Edition p. 716.

Mini-Project

Linear Interpolation by Graphing
(p. 302 of this booklet)

Use With Lesson 13-6.

Objective Use the process of linear interpolation to find values of the sine function between whole number angles.

Materials

grid paper
calculator*
* = available in Overhead Manipulative Resources

Tell students that it is sometimes necessary to find the value of a trigonometric function between whole number angles. This Mini-Project deals with making a graph to interpolate to find the values for each 10-minute interval between the sin 27 degrees and the sin 28 degrees.

Divide students into groups of 2 or 3. Have them read the directions for Exercises 1–4. They may need assistance with setting up the scales for the *x*- and *y*-axes. Use the suggested scale 0.0020 for the *y*-axis. Check their graphs. Ask them to complete Exercise 4 by first reading the values from their graph. Then have them use a calculator to find the values. Ask students to compare the values from the graph with the values from the calculator.

Answers

1–3. Check students' work.

4a. Sample answer: 0.457

4b. Sample answer: 0.459

4c. Sample answer: 0.462

4d. Sample answer: 0.464

4e. Sample answer: 0.467

NAME _____ DATE _____ PERIOD ____

Algebra Activity Transparency Master

(Use with Algebra 2, Lesson 13-1)

Indirect Measurement

HYPSOMETER

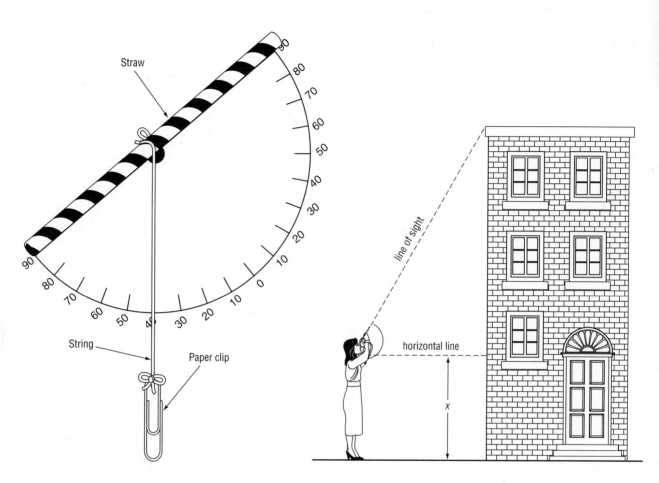

Place on the edge of the index card.

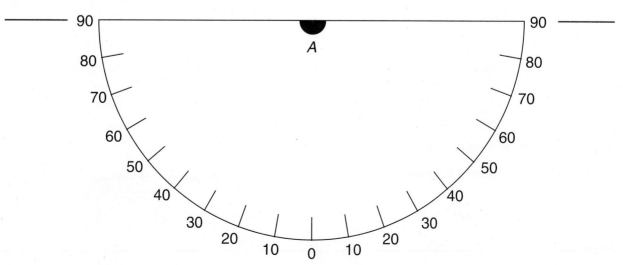

Algebra Activity

(Use with Algebra 2, Lesson 13-1)

Indirect Measurement

Find the height of each object. Use a calculator to find the approximate value of the tangent of the angle.

Example:

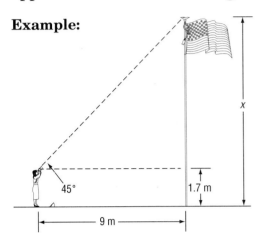

$$\tan (45°) = \frac{x - 1.7}{9}$$
$$1.0 = \frac{x - 1.7}{9}$$
$$9 = x - 1.7$$
$$10.7 = x$$

The flag pole is 10.7 meters high.

1.

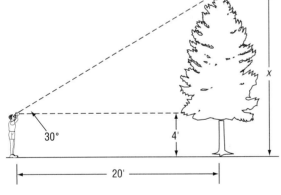

2.

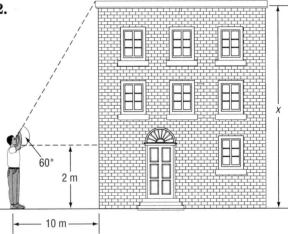

3. Your school building _____

4. The flag pole _____

5. A house close to your school _____

6. A telephone or electric pole _____

7. A church or business building _____

8. Another object _____ _____
         (name of object)   (height of object)

Teaching Algebra with Manipulatives

Algebra Activity Recording Sheet

(Use with the Lesson 13-2 Follow-Up Activity on page 716 in the Student Edition.)

Investigating Regular Polygons Using Trigonometry

Materials: compass, protractor, straightedge

Analyze the Data

1. Complete the table below by recording the length of the apothem of the equilateral triangle.

Number of Sides, *n*	θ	a
3	60	
4	45	
5		
6		
7		
8		
9		
10		

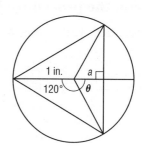

Inscribe each regular polygon named in the table in a circle of radius one inch. Copy and complete the table.

2. What do you notice about the measure of θ as the number of sides of the inscribed polygon increases?

3. What do you notice about the values of *a*?

Make a Conjecture

4. Suppose you inscribe a 20-sided regular polygon inside a circle. Find the measure of angle θ.

5. Write a formula that gives the measure of angle θ for a polygon with *n* sides.

6. Write a formula that gives the length of the apothem of a regular polygon inscribed in a circle of radius one inch.

7. How would the formula you wrote in Exercise 6 change if the radius of the circle was not one inch?

Mini-Project

(Use with Algebra 2, Lesson 13-6)

Linear Interpolation by Graphing

The graph of the function $y = \sin x$ is a smooth curve. When you use the process of interpolation to find a value that is not on a chart, you are actually finding a value on the straight line connecting the known values from a chart.

Suppose you have a chart that represents $\sin x$ for whole number angles. You could create a graph to "interpolate" to find values for each 10 minutes.

Interpolate between sin 27° (0.4540) and sin 28° (0.4695) by following the procedure below.

1. On the grid below, mark the *x*-axis with values 27°, 27°10′, 27°20′, ..., 28°.

2. On the *y*-axis, mark values between 0.4500 and 0.4700 (suggested scale 0.0020).

3. Plot sin 27° at 0.4540 and sin 28° at 0.4695. Connect with a line segment.

4. Read values for the following from your graph. Check against calculator values. (You must change minutes to decimal form. To do this, divide the minutes by 60.)

    a. sin 27°10′

    b. sin 27°20′

    c. sin 27°30′

    d. sin 27°40′

    e. sin 27°50′

14 Trigonometric Graphs and Identities
Teaching Notes and Overview

Mini-Project
Trigonomessage
(p. 304 of this booklet)

Use With Lesson 14-7.

Objective Solve trigonometric equations.

Form groups of two or three students to solve the equations and find the letter that goes with each exercise number. Point out to students that most trigonometric equations, like some algebraic equations, are true for *some* but not *all* values of the variable. Have them check their solutions. Have a reward for each group that discovers the secret message. As a class, go over the solutions. Call on students to show and explain their solutions. There may be students interested in developing a similar type of Mini-Project activity using different equations and decoding a secret message. Students will learn a great deal from developing such an activity.

Answers

1. 300; L

2. −45; S

3. 90; D

4. 120; T

5. 150; I

6. 30; M

7. 210; E

8. 0; N

9. 300; L

10. 210; E

11. −30; G

12. 240; H
message: MEETING AT SMALL SHED

Algebra 2—Chapter 14

Mini-Project

(Use with Algebra 2, Lesson 14-7)

Trigonomessage

Solve each equation for all values of x for the given interval. Then starting at zero, move the indicated degrees on the circle. Place the letter in the blank above the exercise number in the message.

	Degrees	Letter
1. $\dfrac{\sin^2 x}{\cos x} + \cos x = 2;\ 270° < x < 360°$	_____	_____
2. $\tan^2 x = 1;\ -90° < x < 0°$	_____	_____
3. $\csc x + \cos x = 1;\ 0° < x < 180°$	_____	_____
4. $\cos\left(\dfrac{x}{2}\right) = 1 - \cos\left(\dfrac{x}{2}\right);\ 0° < x < 360°$	_____	_____
5. $3\cos 2x = \dfrac{3}{2};\ 90° < x < 180°$	_____	_____
6. $3 - 3\sin x - 2\cos^2 x = 0;\ 0° < x < 90°$	_____	_____
7. $2\sin x + 1 = 0;\ 180° < x < 270°$	_____	_____
8. $\cos 2x + \sin x = 1;\ 0° < x < 90°$	_____	_____
9. $3\tan^2 x = 1;\ 180° < x < 360°$	_____	_____
10. $\sin 2x = 1;\ -90° < x < 90°$	_____	_____
11. $\sin 5x + \sin 7x = 0;\ -45° < x < 0°$	_____	_____
12. $2\cos x + 1 = 0;\ 180° < x < 360°$	_____	_____

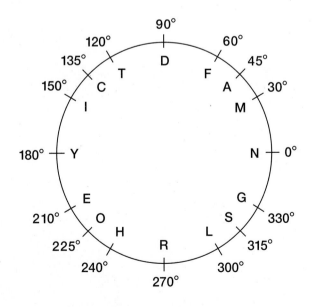

Here is the secret message!!!!

$\overline{}\ \overline{}\ \overline{}\ \overline{}\ \overline{}\ \overline{}\ \overline{}$
6 9 7 4 5 8 11

$\overline{}\ \overline{}$
10 4

$\overline{}\ \overline{}\ \overline{}\ \overline{}\ \overline{}$
2 6 10 1 1

$\overline{}\ \overline{}\ \overline{}\ \overline{}$
2 12 7 3